Learning About Government

by
John Napp

American Guidance Service, Inc.
4201 Woodland Road
Circle Pines, MN 55014-1796
1-800-328-2560

Learning About Our United States

W9-APH-963

Cover photo credit: Images © 1996 Photo Disc, Inc.

© 1997 by AGS® American Guidance Service, Inc., Circle Pines, MN 55014-1796. All rights reserved, including translation. No part of this publication may be reproduced or transmitted in any form or by any means without written permission from the publisher.

Printed in the United States of America

ISBN 0–7854–0961–0 (Previously ISBN 0–88671–972–0)

Order Number: 90872

A 0 9 8 7

Contents

Early Government in Colonial America

In 1607, English settlers established the colony of Jamestown in Virginia. This was the first successful English colony in North America. These settlers brought with them their English traditions and laws. These would serve as the building blocks for the democratic form of government established in the United States.

The House of Burgesses

The **House of Burgesses,** established in Jamestown in 1619, was the first representative legislature in what is now the United States. It was made up of two elected representatives from each of eleven settled parts of Virginia. Together with the appointed governor and his council, the house made up the General Assembly of Virginia. This assembly made laws that were in the best interest of the settlers. As time passed, the practice of **representation** became the foundation of our system of government.

The Mayflower Compact

The Pilgrims landed at Plymouth, Massachusetts, in 1620. Their trip from England was made aboard the *Mayflower.* Storms and rough waters carried the small ship far off course. The Pilgrims decided to land and settle in an area for which they did not have a charter. A charter was a government document that enabled colonists to settle in a specific place. Without a charter, they needed to establish policies of their own. The Pilgrims wrote the **Mayflower Compact.** The Pilgrims who signed the compact agreed to follow all the laws that were passed by the majority of the settlers. The Mayflower Compact was important because it gave the power of governing to the people. In the years to follow, this system would become the cornerstone of our government.

British Colonies in America

The British colonies in Colonial America could make their own laws, raise taxes, and set up their own court system. The British governors could overrule the colonial governments but usually did not interfere. In later years, when trouble began between the British and the Americans, this changed.

The northern New England Colonies were made up of small farms and many small towns. The towns elected their own officials and made their own laws. The salaries paid to the people who ran the government came from taxes collected from the residents. The people took part in the town meetings because the towns were so small. The beginnings of a democratic form of government were established in those early northern colonies.

In the Southern Colonies, farms were larger and the towns were farther apart. The area was divided into counties. A county was a large area that included many small towns. Town meetings, such as those in New England, were not used. It was much harder for residents to be involved in the government because they lived so far apart. The governor appointed public officials to manage the affairs of the county.

UNIT 1

The Middle Colonies practiced a mixture of the two systems. Some had town meetings, and others had the county system. Coincidentally, the three groups of colonies all developed the democratic approach to government.

Write your answer to the following questions.

1. List three important facts about the House of Burgesses.

   a. ______________________________

   b. ______________________________

   c. ______________________________

2. Why was the Mayflower Compact written? ______________________________

   ____

   ____

   ____

3. Why was New England well suited for town meetings?

   ____

   ____

   ____

4. Why was it hard to hold town meetings in the Southern Colonies?

   ____

   ____

   ____

5. **Special Thought Question:** The Middle Colonies had a mixture of town meetings and county government. Why do you think this happened?

   ____

   ____

   ____

   ____

   ____

Call for Colonial Unity

In the 1700s, the French, who had settled in what is now Canada, and the British were interested in the same land—land west of the British colonies to the Mississippi River. Disagreements between the two countries would lead to war. The British colonists were concerned about protection. What could they do?

The Albany Plan

In 1754, a convention was held in Albany, New York. The purpose of the convention was to decide how the colonies would defend themselves from the French. The leader of the convention was Benjamin Franklin. He suggested that a congress be formed and that the colonies send representatives to the congress. It would make treaties with various tribes, collect taxes for an army, and oversee how western lands were settled. In this way, the colonies would work together to defend themselves. Franklin's ideas were called the *Albany Plan.*

The Albany delegates, representatives sent to the convention by the colonies, approved the plan, but not one colonial assembly accepted it. The plan failed. There were too many differences between the colonies, especially over the issue of taxation. Even though the plan was not approved, the idea of having a congress and forming a union of colonies had been established.

The colonial leaders knew a union was needed, but they could not agree on how it should be done. A few years later, serious problems with Great Britain, which ruled the British colonies, made a union necessary. The Americans could not longer allow their differences to divide them into thirteen separate colonies.

The First Continental Congress

The British changed their policies toward the colonies after the French and Indian War (1756–1763). The colonies could no longer run their governments as they wanted. Britain passed strict laws, many of them involving taxes, that the colonists had to follow. The colonists were not happy with these changes or with the taxes.

The colonies decided to send delegates to a meeting to discuss the problems. The First Continental Congress met in Philadelphia, Pennsylvania, in September of 1774. The delegates drew up a list of grievances and a Declaration of Rights. A new spirit of cooperation had been established. The representatives agreed to meet again in 1775. When the British king, George III, and Parliament viewed the actions of the colonists as defiance of their rule, many leaders of the colonies knew the time had come for America to declare its independence from Britain.

Ben Franklin suggested the Albany Plan.

UNIT 1

The Declaration of Independence

The **Declaration of Independence** stated that the American colonies were free from British rule. The document was written mainly by Thomas Jefferson in 1776. Educated people such as Thomas Jefferson, James Madison, and John Adams studied the writings of great philosophers. A philosopher is a thinker who writes about very complicated ideas. Philosophers also make theories about how certain things came to be. Thomas Jefferson was greatly influenced by the philosopher John Locke.

John Locke had argued that there is a contract between the government and the people. If the government violates the natural rights of the people, they can rebel and set up a new government. In the Declaration of Independence, Jefferson wrote that all people have certain natural rights, such as "life, liberty, and the pursuit of happiness." If a government does not protect these rights, it loses its right to govern. On the evening of July 4, 1776, the delegates voted to approve the Declaration of Independence.

Write your answers to the following questions.

1. Why did early attempts to form a union fail? ______________________________

____

2. Why was the Albany Convention held? ______________________________

____

3. Even though the Albany Plan was turned down, two important ideas were established. What were those ideas?

a. ____

b. ____

4. What changes did the British make in the American colonies?

a. ____

b. ____

5. Why was the First Continental Congress important to the American colonists?

____

6. Who wrote the Declaration of Independence? ______________________________

7. Why is John Locke important to American government? ______________________________

____

8. What were three rights Jefferson said were natural rights? ______________________________

____

Forming a Government

Although the colonies were willing to cooperate with each other, they were afraid of losing too much individual power. They were used to making their own laws and decisions. They were not eager to turn their government over to someone else.

The Articles of Confederation

The country was governed by the **Articles of Confederation** during the Revolutionary War. The Articles gave the country a chance to test a democratic government. Under the Articles, a legislature, **Congress,** was set up. There was no executive branch or judicial branch of government. Each state was given one vote in the Congress. Nine states had to approve any major decision. The powers given to Congress were very limited and mostly related to the war effort. Congress could wage war, make peace, make treaties, and request troops and money from the states. It could also borrow money. Congress could not levy taxes or regulate trade. It could not force states to contribute money or troops or to obey treaties. The main purpose of the Articles of Confederation was to create a bond of friendship between the states.

It became clear after the war ended in 1783 that the Articles of Confederation were too weak to be effective. Some major changes needed to be made.

The Constitution

In May of 1787, the **Constitutional Convention** began in Philadelphia, Pennsylvania. Fifty-five delegates attended the convention. They planned to change the Articles of Confederation. Instead, they wrote a new document called the **Constitution** of the United States.

Although the delegates had been sent by their states to change the Articles of Confederation, most of them believed that the articles were beyond mending. Most delegates agreed that any new government had to have the authority that Congress lacked under the Articles of Confederation. In particular, the government needed the power to levy taxes, to raise and support armed forces, to regulate trade, and to make and enforce laws. Most also agreed on the importance of separating government functions into branches—legislative, executive, and judicial—as a way to guard against the abuse of power by any one branch. That is about all they agreed on.

The remainder of the Constitutional Convention consisted of debates followed by **compromises.** After compromising on the major issues—state representation in Congress, election of the President, and slavery—the delegates were ready to complete their work. On September 17, 1787, the Constitution was read to the convention. Thirty-nine delegates signed it. Then the people at the state level had to approve, or **ratify,** the Constitution for it to take effect. In 1788, eleven states had ratified it. By the spring of 1790, all thirteen states had ratified the Constitution.

UNIT 1

Review Unit 1

Write your answer to the following questions.

1. Why did the colonies decide they needed to work together under some written plan?

2. Under the Articles of Confederation, what branch of government was set up?

3. What were three things Congress could do under the Articles of Confederation?

4. What were two things Congress could not do under the Articles of Confederation?

5. When did the Revolutionary War end?
6. Why did the Articles of Confederation need to be changed?

7. When and where was the Constitutional Convention held?

8. How many delegates attended the Constitutional Convention?
9. How many branches of government were set up? What were they called?

10. How did the delegates reach agreement on issues that divided them?

11. What was the result of the convention?

12. How many delegates signed the Constitution?

Identifying Types of Government

Governments are usually identified as **unitary, confederate,** or **federal.** The United States has a federal government. At one time, the United States had a confederate government. The country was governed by the Articles of Confederation during the Revolutionary War.

A confederate government gives more power to the individual states and less power to the central government. The confederate system lasted until the present Constitution went into effect in 1789. During the Civil War, the Southern States referred to themselves as the Confederacy.

Unitary Government
Many countries in the world have a unitary system of government. One example of a country with a unitary government is the United Kingdom (Great Britain).

All of the power is held by the central government in the unitary system. The central government can decide if a local government (cities or counties) is needed. The local government can also be eliminated if the central government chooses to do so.

The British Government
In the British unitary system, there is a **Parliament.** The Parliament is similar to the Congress in the United States. However, the Parliament is made up of both the **legislative** (lawmaking) branch and **executive** (law enforcing) branch of the government.

The Parliament has two houses. The House of Lords has over 1,000 members. The members are not elected. The more powerful House of Commons has over 600 members. These members are elected by the people of the United Kingdom. An election must be held at least once every five years. The House of Commons chooses the prime minister. The prime minister is similar to the President of the United States. The prime minister can serve for many years.

If serious problems should occur during the prime minister's term or if there is dissatisfaction with the way the prime minister is performing, a "vote of confidence" can be required by the House of Commons. The prime minister and his or her cabinet must resign if the vote is less than a majority. If this happens, a new election is usually held soon after, and all the seats in the House of Commons are open for re-election.

UNIT 2

A Complete the following exercise.

1. List three different types of government.
   a. ____________________
   b. ____________________
   c. ____________________
2. Which type of government does the United States have?
   ____
3. When did the United States have a confederate type of government? ____________________
   ____
4. In the confederate type of government, are the state governments stronger or weaker than the central government?
   ____
   ____
5. Many countries have a unitary type of government.
   Give an example of a country that has this type of government. ____________________
6. What is the British legislative and executive branch called? ____________________
7. What title is given to the British leader? ____________________
8. How many houses does the British Parliament have?
   What are they called?
   ____
   ____
   ____
9. How many members does each house have? ____________________
   ____
10. How and why can the prime minister be replaced in Parliament? ____________________
    ____
    ____
    ____
    ____

UNIT 2

B Fill in each blank with the correct term. Choose the answer from the word box.

Word Box

election	Great Britain
House of Commons	executive
vote of confidence	prime minister
central	resign
United Kingdom	legislative
local	Congress

The Unitary Type of Government

A very good example of a country with a unitary type of government is the ____________ ____________,which is sometimes called by the name of ____________ ____________. All of the power is held by the ____________ government. ____________ governments, such as those for cities and counties, may or may not be needed.

The British Parliament is similar to our ____________. The Parliament, however, is made up of both the ____________ (lawmaking) branch and the ____________ (law enforcing) branch of government.

The people of the United Kingdom elect all of the members of the ____________ ____ ____________. These members, in turn, elect a ____________ ____________. If serious problems develop in the leadership of the government, a ____________ ____ ____________ can be required. If the prime minister does not get a majority, he or she must ____________. A new ____________ is usually held at that time for all of the elected officials of the Parliament.

The Federal System

The delegates to the Constitutional Convention had a hard time deciding what kind of government would work best for the new country. A major issue was **representation.** People wanted to have a say in their government. They were concerned that the central government would be too powerful. They wanted the central government to have the power it needed and not take all the power away from the states.

The delegates made many compromises. Finally, they agreed on a federal government. They wrote a document called the Constitution of the United States. The Constitution is called the *Supreme Law of the Land.* The Constitution limits the power of both the central government and the state governments. Power is shared by the central government and the state governments. People elect representatives (officials) at all levels of government.

In the United States, there are three levels of government. The central government runs the country's major programs, such as defense and foreign policy. The state governments take care of most of their own state affairs. The states are divided into smaller units, or **local governments,** such as county governments and city governments. Most of these smaller units take care of local affairs. This three-level system has worked well for over 200 years.

Delegates to the Constitutional Convention met at the Pennsylvania State House, now called Independence Hall.

UNIT 2

A Complete the following exercise by writing one fact about each of the terms listed below.

1. the Constitution ________________________________

____

2. representation ________________________________

____

3. compromises ________________________________

____

4. central government ________________________________

____

5. state government ________________________________

____

6. local government ________________________________

____

B In a brief paragraph, explain how the three-level system of government in the United States is organized.

____

____

____

____

____

____

____

____

____

____

____

____

UNIT 2

Separation of Powers

The delegates to the Constitutional Convention were concerned that too much power would be controlled by a few people. They thought the king of Great Britain had too much power. They did not want the same kind of government. The king, with his advisers and Parliament, passed laws for the colonies. These laws were often harmful to the colonists. The colonists wanted a government in which the power was divided.

This was accomplished by establishing three separate branches of government. Each branch was given certain powers and limitations. The **executive** branch (the President) enforces the laws, the **legislative** branch (Congress) makes the laws, and the **judicial** branch (courts) interprets the laws. This is called **separation of powers.**

Each branch was connected through a system of **checks and balances.** Each branch of power "checks up" on the actions of the other branches. There are six basic relationships under the checks-and-balances system. The following chart illustrates the relationships.

The System of Checks and Balances

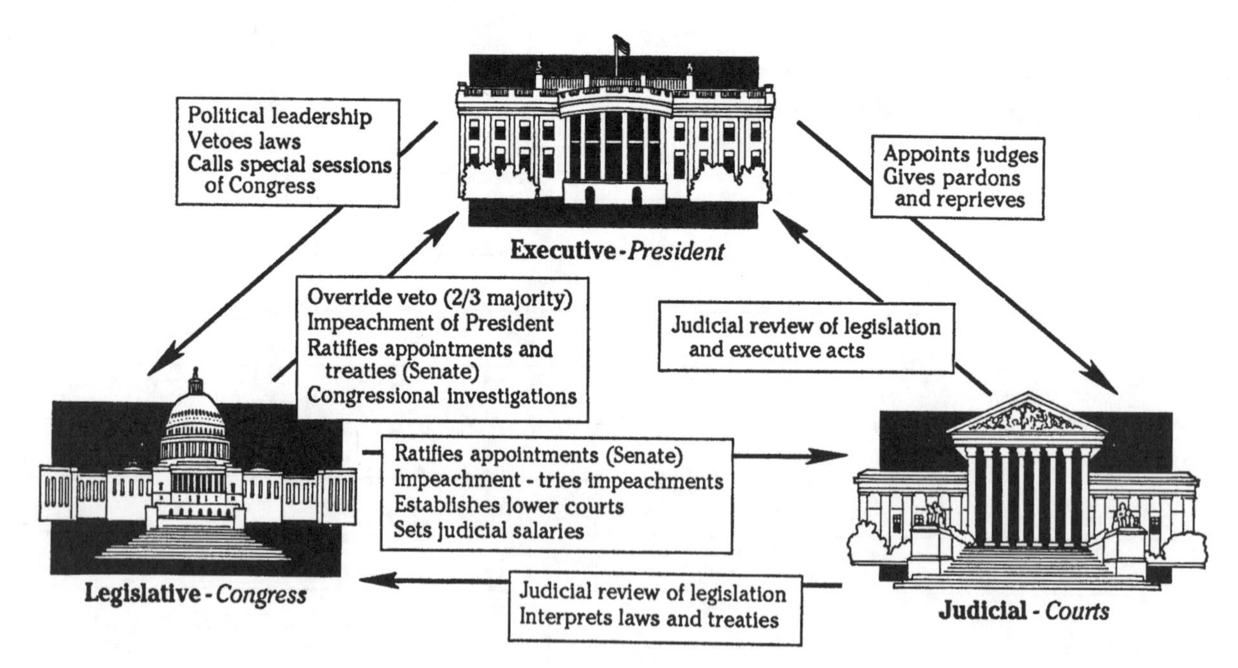

A Complete the following exercise.

1. List the three branches of our government. What does each do?

   a. ______________________________

   ____

   b. ______________________________

   ____

   c. ______________________________

   ____

2. Why were the three branches of government established? ______________________________

   ____

3. What does separation of powers mean? ______________________________

   ____

B Use the diagram "The System of Checks and Balances" on page 16 to answer the following questions. Write your answer in the space provided. Use the following letters for your answers:

a. executive   b. legislative   c. judicial

_____ 1. Which branch of government appoints federal judges?

_____ 2. Which branch of government can declare a law unconstitutional?

_____ 3. Which branch of government can veto legislation (bills)?

_____ 4. Which branch of government can override the President's veto?

_____ 5. Which branch of government can approve or turn down appointment of judges?

_____ 6. Which branch of government can declare executive acts to be unconstitutional?

_____ 7. Which branch of government conducts investigations when problems occur?

The Constitution Changes

In 1789, when the Constitution went into effect, the United States had only thirteen states. Over the years, our country has grown. Now, more than 200 years later, there are 50 states. The United States has changed a great deal over those 200 years. How did the Constitution continue to serve the people so well during all this time and through all the changes? The language used in the Constitution could be interpreted to mean different things as times changed. Also, the Constitution could be changed by adding **amendments** that dealt with specific issues not discussed in the original document. The Constitution was meant to be a flexible document, safeguarding our basic freedoms and changing with the needs of the times.

Amendments

James Madison felt that the rights of citizens needed to be protected. He suggested that ten amendments be added to the Constitution. These amendments are known as the **Bill of Rights.** They were added to the Constitution in 1791. They identify some of the rights of the people and how they are protected from possible harmful acts by the government.

Over the years, seventeen more amendments have been added. The process for adding amendments is not an easy one. By making the amendment process difficult, the framers of the Constitution hoped to prevent sudden changes that might not be wise.

Amendment	Subject
1	Guarantees freedom of religion, of speech, and of the press; the right to peaceful assembly; the right to petition government.
2	Guarantees the right to possess weapons.
3	States that citizens are not required to house soldiers during peacetime or during war, except as provided by law.
4	Protects people from unreasonable searches and seizures.
5	Guarantees due process of law; protects accused people from double jeopardy and from being forced to testify against themselves.
6	Guarantees the right to a trial by jury in criminal cases; the right to question witnesses; the right to be assisted by a lawyer.
7	Guarantees the right to a trial by jury in most civil cases.
8	Prohibits excessive bail, fines, and punishments.
9	Declares that rights not mentioned in the Constitution belong to the people.
10	States that powers not given to the federal government belong to the states or to the people.

Review Unit 2

A Write one fact about each of the items listed below.

1. 1789 ______________________________

2. thirteen states ______________________________

3. fifty states ______________________________

4. amendments ______________________________

5. flexible document ______________________________

6. Bill of Rights ______________________________

7. James Madison ______________________________

B Write your answer to the following questions.

1. When was the Bill of Rights added to the Constitution? ______________________________
2. Who proposed the amendments? ______________________________
3. How many amendments does the Bill of Rights have? ______________________________
4. Why were they added? ______________________________
5. How many more amendments have been added to the Constitution since the Bill of Rights? ______________________________
6. Why is the amendment process not an easy one? ______________________________

C Our federal system of government has worked well for over 200 years. The unitary system of government of the United Kingdom has also worked well for a long time. Compare the two types of government using the chart below.

Unitary	Federal
Advantages ______ ______ ______ ______ ______ ______ ______	**Advantages** ______ ______ ______ ______ ______ ______ ______
Disadvantages ______ ______ ______ ______ ______ ______ ______	**Disadvantages** ______ ______ ______ ______ ______ ______ ______

D Write the number of the amendment that protects people in the situations that follow.

_____ **1.** Li wants to protest the building of a landfill near her home.

_____ **2.** The police asked to search Donald's apartment. They had no warrant.

_____ **3.** Jason wanted a jury to decide his lawsuit in court.

_____ **4.** Emma's lawyer told her she did not have to testify during her trial.

_____ **5.** Juan decided to go to a different church than the one he usually attended.

The Constitutional Convention

Lesson 1

The Articles of Confederation guided the new country through the Revolutionary War (1776–1783) and a few years beyond. The Articles of Confederation gave the central government very little power. Arguments between the states could not be settled. The central government could not raise enough money to run the country properly. Changes in the document were needed.

The Constitutional Convention was called in 1787 to fix the Articles of Confederation. Instead, a new Constitution was written. Many issues were debated during the Constitutional Convention. These debates contributed to the development of **political parties.** How strong should the *central government* be? How strong should the *state governments* be? Each of these questions had its supporters. Those who favored a strong central government were called **Federalists.** Those who favored strong state governments were called **Anti-Federalists.**

The First President

The new country needed a new government system. A President who would guide the country successfully was also needed. George Washington was **unanimously** elected to be the first President. That means every **elector,** or member of the electoral college that votes for the President, voted for Washington. He was greatly respected as a leader. Washington was considered to be the best person for the office. John Adams, a Federalist from Massachusetts, became the first Vice President. They turned their attention to shaping the new government.

George Washington believed that the country should have a strong central government. He was concerned that political parties would hurt the country. He thought that elected officials should all work together.

George Washington served two terms as President and then retired.

The Election of 1796

The first hint of a **two-party system** of government was during the 1796 presidential election. John Adams won the election by a small margin of votes from the electors. Thomas Jefferson had the second most votes and became Vice President. During that time in America's history, the person who came in second automatically became Vice President. Jefferson and Adams had two very different political views. Adams was a Federalist, and Jefferson was an Anti-Federalist, or **Democratic-Republican.** The two parties were very different. The Federalists wanted a strong central government, and the Democratic-Republicans wanted state governments to be stronger. The President and Vice President were political opponents.

The Election of 1800

John Adams had become very unpopular by the time of the 1800 election. He still decided to run for re-election. Adams, Thomas Jefferson, and Aaron Burr were the three major candidates. Jefferson and Burr were both Democratic-Republicans, and each received 73 electoral votes. The House of Representatives decided who would be President. They chose Jefferson. Burr became Vice President. Adams received only 65 electoral votes, so he lost the election.

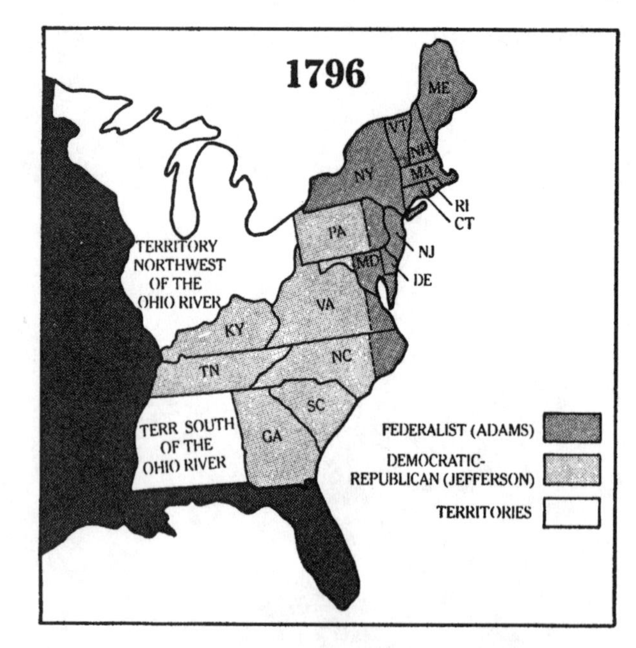

John Adams received 71 electoral votes to win the 1796 presidential election. Thomas Jefferson received 68 electoral votes. He became Vice President.

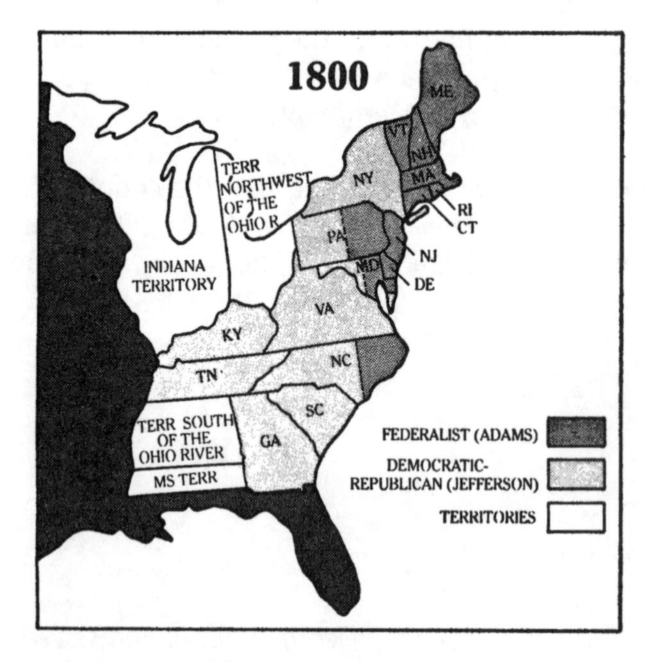

Thomas Jefferson opposed John Adams again in the 1800 election. Jefferson with 73 electoral votes was chosen President by the House of Representatives. Aaron Burr, with 73 electoral votes, became Vice President. Adams had 65 electoral votes.

Fill in each blank with the correct term or date. Choose the answer from the word box.

Word Box

states	Constitutional Convention	Democratic-Republican
Federalists	1776–1783	Anti-Federalists
money	Articles of Confederation	changes
Anti-Federalist	Federalist	

The Constitutional Convention and Beyond

During the Revolutionary War (______________), the government of our country was guided by the ______________ ________ ______________.

The central government was very weak and could not settle arguments between the ______________. The central government also could not raise enough ______________ to run the country properly. Some ______________ needed to be made to the Articles of Confederation.

In 1787, the ______________ ______________ was held to fix the Articles of Confederation. The major question was how strong the central government should be. Those who favored a strong government were called ______________. Those who favored a strong state government were called ______________. The plan to change the Articles of Confederation was thrown out, and a new Constitution was written.

In the election of 1796, Adams, a ______________, and Jefferson, an ______________, also called a ______________ ______________, was elected Vice President.

Political Parties and Democracy

George Washington did not like the idea of political parties. He believed that political parties would divide the country. In his Farewell Address in 1796, Washington warned against the "continual mischiefs" of political parties. That is how much he disliked the idea of political parties. However, political parties are now very much a part of our democratic system of government.

The Two-Party System

In a democracy, many different points of view need to be heard. In the beginning, the country was very small. As time passed, the country became larger in area and in population. Many new and different ideas were developed.

Political parties try to represent most of the separate interests. This is not easy to do. The two current **major parties** are the **Democratic Party** and the **Republican Party.** Both parties try to get as much support as they can. Voters are free to choose the party and the issues they wish to support. Voters are also free to switch **candidates,** people running for political offices, or parties if they are unhappy with the performance of elected officials. This choice is the basis of a democracy. The people are free to choose the candidate they think will represent them the best. A party that fails to meet the needs of voters can expect little support.

From time to time, third parties, sometimes called **minor parties,** are formed to represent people with particular points of view. This is also a part of the democratic process. In many elections, there are more than two parties on the ballot, but the Republican and Democratic parties are the largest and strongest.

Party Organization

The most important goal of a political party is to win elected offices. Each of the two major parties hopes to win many elections. In order to win, the party must be well organized. The parties need to have good candidates. Men and women who appeal to the voters and represent the views of their party are encouraged to run for **public office.** The two political parties choose a slate of candidates, that is, a list of people from their party that they would like to see elected to each political office for which there is an opening. This is especially true in state and local elections. Of course, anyone who meets the qualifications can run for office.

Candidates campaign for people's votes. They make many speeches explaining what they think about the important issues. Elections are very expensive for a candidate. A campaign staff is organized to help the candidate get elected. The staff raises money to pay for advertising and other election expenses. One of the most expensive parts of an election is buying television time. To get the message out, it is important for the candidate to be seen and heard.

Volunteer help is another important part of a political campaign. In addition to donating money, volunteers often offer their time and help in a variety of ways. Working with the party organization, they might make telephone calls reminding people to vote for a particular candidate. They might put up posters and hand out campaign flyers, or they might give people rides to the polls on election day. There are many ways to support a candidate or party. This, too, is part of the democratic process.

A Write a brief summary using each of the words listed below. You may use the words in any order.

political parties	Republican
democracy	candidates
voter	Democratic

____

____

____

____

____

B Why are the following activities important in party organization? Write a brief comment about each.

1. raising money ______________________________

____

2. attracting good candidates ______________________________

____

3. winning elections ______________________________

____

C List two ways you could help in a political campaign.

1. ______________________________

____

2. ______________________________

____

Minor Parties

Even though the government in the United States is considered to be a two-party system, minor parties have existed. The Free Soil Party of the 1840s, the Prohibition Party in 1872, the Socialist Party of the 1880s, the Populist Party in the 1890s, the Progressive Party in 1912, and the Reform Party in the 1990s are all examples. Generally, these parties last only a short time. The Socialist Party and the Prohibition Party, however, were active for quite a while.

Importance of Minor Parties

Minor parties usually have special issues that are important to their followers. For example, Free Soil followers did not want slavery in the new states. The Socialist Party wanted major social programs, such as Social Security, unemployment insurance, and stronger labor unions. Those ideas were later adopted by the Democratic Party and are in effect today.

Minor parties have always been important to the political system. New ideas are often too risky for the major parties to support. It takes time for new ideas to be discussed and understood by the people. Minor parties do not usually win elections. However, they have made contributions to the democratic system of government.

The Election of 1912

This map illustrates the influence that a minority party had on a national election. The three parties involved were the Democratic, Progressive, and Republican.

UNIT 3

A Make a list of five minor parties and the time period of each.

1. ______________________________
2. ______________________________
3. ______________________________
4. ______________________________
5. ______________________________

B Answer the following questions.

1. How are minor parties different from major parties? ______________________________

____

____

2. Why are minor parties important? ______________________________

____

3. Candidates of minor parties usually do not win major elections. Why?

____

____

____

C Write your answer to the questions that follow.

1. If you were to start a minor party, what would you call it? Why?

____

____

2. What are two major issues that would be a part of your party's platform?

____

____

Political Parties Today

The two major parties try to cover all important issues that concern the general public. There are some differences, however, between the two parties.

Liberal vs. Conservative

Many people consider the Democrats to be more **liberal** than the Republicans and the Republicans to be more **conservative** than the Democrats. This comparison is very often used between the two parties. Yet, there are liberal Republicans and conservative Democrats. Liberals want to see changes take place quickly. They often support government control of the economy and social programs that will help make people's lives better. Many also believe that individual freedoms must be protected. Conservatives, on the other hand, prefer to make changes more slowly. Many believe that the economy works better when there is little government interference with it. Some believe that the need to protect society is of greater importance than individual freedoms.

Using the labels *conservative* and *liberal* to identify a party or person is very confusing. Political parties and voters can be liberal on one issue and conservative on another. Some are **moderate,** or in the middle—not conservative or liberal—on many positions.

There are several reasons that help explain why people vote as they do. The United States is very large. It is made up of many different geographical regions. The needs of these regions are not the same. Each region is made up of people of various backgrounds. Their ages, the work they do, and even current world affairs all have an effect on how people view the major political issues of the country. These factors, in turn, can affect why people vote and for whom.

Political Symbols

The donkey is used to represent the Democratic Party. Many Democrats view their symbol as humble and "down home."

The elephant is used to represent the Republican Party. Many Republicans view their symbol as strong and intelligent.

Review Unit 3

Fill in the blank with the correct term or number. Choose the answer from the word box.

Word Box

conservative	liberal	Republicans
Democrats	two	democratic
minor	major	200
quickly	slowly	confusing
moderate		

Political Parties Today

The United States has had a ____________________ system of government for more than ____________________ years. During that period of time, a variety of ____________________ and ____________________ parties have existed. At present, we have ____________________ major political parties. The members of one party are called the ____________________ and the members of the other party are called the ____________________. Very often, the Democratic Party is called the ____________________ party. They want to see changes take place ____________________. The Republican Party is called the ____________________ party. They want to see changes take place more ____________________. These definitions are often much too ____________________. Many Democrats and Republicans are ____________________ on many issues. People can be liberal on some issues and conservative on other issues.

B As a class, make a list of five issues that are important in our country today. Do you think students in other parts of our country would have similar issues? Why might their lists be different from yours? Discuss your opinions with your class.

1. ______________________________
2. ______________________________
3. ______________________________
4. ______________________________
5. ______________________________

REVIEW

Review Units 1–3

A Write the letter of the word from the box that is being defined.

Word Box

a. candidate	d. Constitution
b. amendments	e. Federalists
c. Congress	f. unanimous

_____ 1. those who favored a strong central government

_____ 2. the supreme law of the land

_____ 3. additions to the Constitution

_____ 4. agreed to by everyone

_____ 5. one who seeks a public office

_____ 6. legislative branch of the federal government

B Write *True* or *False* on the line before each statement.

__________ 1. There is little the average person can do to help a candidate win an election.

__________ 2. Great Britain has a unitary system of government.

__________ 3. The Articles of Confederation provided for a strong central government.

__________ 4. Minor parties rarely win elections.

__________ 5. The Constitution has never been changed.

__________ 6. Conservatives favor quick changes in the government.

__________ 7. Issues that minor parties raise are rarely important.

__________ 8. George Washington was a strong supporter of the two-party system.

__________ 9. Liberals often support government control of the economy.

Congress

The Constitution established three separate branches of government—the legislative branch, the executive branch, and the judicial branch. The branch that will be discussed in this unit is the legislative branch. This branch is also known as **Congress.**

Congress Is Bicameral

The delegates at the Constitutional Convention decided that the government should have a two-house legislative body. This is called **bicameral.** The two houses are the **House of Representatives** and the **Senate.** (If there was a one-house legislative body, it would be called **unicameral.**)

The Convention delegates decided on the organization of the two houses. The number of members in the **lower house,** the House of Representatives, would be determined by the population of each individual state. States with larger populations would have more members in the House. Currently the House of Representatives has 435 members.

The **upper house,** the Senate, is organized differently. Each state, regardless of its population, has two senators. States would have equal representation in the Senate. Today, the Senate has 100 members—two for each of the 50 states. The first Congress of the United States had 65 members in the House of Representatives and 26 members in the Senate.

The Constitution gave Congress certain powers. Among them are the power to tax, to regulate trade between states and with foreign countries, to borrow money, to coin money, and to establish lower federal courts. Other powers include raising an army and navy, maintaining the armed forces, and declaring war. Although the President may ask Congress to declare war, only a vote of Congress can result in a formal declaration of war.

The Constitution also limits the powers Congress has. Congress may not pass trade laws that favor one state over another. The Bill of Rights forbids Congress from making other laws, such as the establishment of a national religion or limiting freedom of speech or the press.

UNIT 4

A List the names of the two houses of the United States Congress.

1. ______________________________

2. ______________________________

B Fill in each blank with the correct term or number. Choose an answer from the word box.

Word Box

65	Senate	House of Representatives
population	Congress	two
bicameral	26	tax
war	trade	courts

Congress—The Legislative Branch

The legislative branch of our government is called the ________________. It is a ________________ legislature because it has two houses. The lower house is called the ________________ ____ ________________. The upper house is called the ________________. The number of members in the lower house is determined by the ________________ of a state. The number of members in the upper house is equal: ________________ from each state. The first Congress had ________________ members in the lower house and ________________ members in the upper house.

Of the three branches of government, only Congress has the power to ________________, to regulate ________________, to establish lower federal ________________, and to declare ________________.

The House of Representatives

The terms *upper house* and *lower house* do not mean that one house is more important than the other. It simply means that the members of the House of Representatives serve only a portion of their state's population. The members of the Senate, on the other hand, serve the entire state. Representatives are elected every two years. Senators are elected every six years.

The people who serve in the House of Representatives are called *representatives* or **congressmen** or **congresswomen.** To be eligible to become a representative, a person must—

- be at least 25 years of age.
- be a citizen of the United States for at least seven years.
- live in the state or congressional district he or she represents.

Term of Office

A representative is elected for a two-year **term.** The short term was intended to make the House of Representatives act quickly on important issues and to make them more responsive to the people they represent. The brief term places the elected official in a **vulnerable,** open to criticism and possible loss of office, position. The people can voice their opinions when they vote. The representatives may not be re-elected if the voters are not pleased with their job performance.

A new Congress begins every time the House of Representatives is elected. Congressional elections are held in even numbered years.

Each representative has a staff that helps keep the citizens of his or her state informed about the current issues being discussed.

The U.S. Capitol Building in Washington, D. C., is where Congress makes the laws.

UNIT 4

Review Unit 4

A List three qualifications that a person needs to have in order to serve in the House of Representatives.

1. ______
2. ______
3. ______

B Write your answers to the questions that follow.

1. What are two reasons the framers of the Constitution decided to make the term of a member of the House of Representatives two years?

   a. ______

   b. ______

2. Why is the position of representative vulnerable?

   ______

3. What is one thing you would like your representative to change or improve?

   ______

4. **Special Thought Question:** Some people think that the term of two years is too short for members of the House of Representatives. They recommend that it be changed to at least four years. What do you think?

   ______

Congressional Districts

The United States Congress has 435 representatives. This number was determined in 1929 and is not likely to change in the near future. The states are divided into congressional **districts.** The districts contain approximately the same number of people. The number of representatives each state has depends on its population. A ratio of the states' population to the national population determines the exact number of representatives per state.

Because the population of the United States changes, **reapportionment** of the house seats takes place every ten years after the **census** is taken. That means that the districts are reorganized to keep them equal.

Some states attract more people than others. California, Florida, Texas, and Arizona are states that have grown very fast. These states have gained representatives in recent years. Sometimes, states decrease (lessen) in population. These states may lose representatives. Regardless of a state's population, each state is guaranteed at least one representative. Therefore, it is necessary to reorganize the districts. The party, either Democrat or Republican, that is in the majority (over 50 percent) decides on how the reapportionment should be done.

The House of Representatives has some very specific powers. For example, the House can **impeach,** or accuse of wrongdoing, a federal official, such as the President, a cabinet member, or a Supreme Court justice. The House of Representatives also elects the President if the electoral college fails to give any candidate a majority.

■ Write a summary paragraph in which you use each of the following words. You may use them in any order.

equal	census
states	district
reapportionment	congressmen
435	congresswomen

____

____

____

____

____

____

____

____

UNIT 4

The Speaker of the House

The **speaker** holds the most important and powerful position in the House of Representatives. The Speaker of the House is the leader of the **majority party.** He or she is chosen by the party because of his or her experience and leadership in the House. The speaker usually serves for several years, providing his or her party remains in the majority. The Speaker of the House is next in line for the presidency after the Vice President. If the President and Vice President should die or leave office during their term, the Speaker of the House would become President. The President, however, can appoint a new Vice President if the Vice President dies or leaves office. As a result, it is unlikely that the Speaker of the House would ever become President.

The speaker's position is very important because he or she has a great deal of power. The 435 members of the House must obey strict rules. The speaker is in charge. No one may address (speak to) the House of Representatives unless the speaker gives permission. Important **bills** (future laws) are greatly influenced by the speaker. It has been said that only the President of the United States has more power than the Speaker of the House of Representatives.

■ Fill in the blank with the correct term or number. Choose the answer from the word box. One word will be used more than once.

Word Box

speaker	rules	Vice President
powerful	majority	President
bills	435	speak

Speaker of the House

The most important and __________________ position in the House of Representatives is the __________________. The two positions that are higher in our government are the __________________ and the __________________ __________________. The __________________ party (over 50 percent) chooses the speaker. The __________________ members of the House must obey strict __________________. No member may __________________ unless he or she has the approval of the speaker. The outcome of important __________________ is greatly influenced by the __________________.

The Senate

Two senators from each state make up the Senate. There are 100 members in the Senate. This number could change if more states are added. The term of office is six years. Qualifications for senators include—

- being at least 30 years of age.
- being a citizen of the United States for at least nine years.
- living in the state from which elected.

The number of senators, the term of office, and the older age requirement are just three of the differences between the House and the Senate. Senators are elected by people throughout an entire state. They represent the whole state, not just a district.

The Senate operates very differently from the House of Representatives. The Vice President of the United States is the president of the Senate. He or she cannot discuss any bill. He or she can only vote if there is a tie. The Vice President is often away on important government business. In the Vice President's place is a **president pro tempore.** This position usually goes to the senator of the majority party who has the longest continuous service. Actually, the president pro tempore rarely presides. Different temporary presidents from the majority party guide the debate in most sessions.

Party leaders in the Senate have many more powers than those specified by the Constitution. The majority party selects the **majority leader** of the Senate, and the other party selects a **minority leader.** In addition, each party chooses an assistant leader called a **whip.** The whip tries to "whip up" support for upcoming bills by trying to persuade senators to vote for the party's position.

The Senate does not have strict rules. Debates (discussions) can go on for several days. This freedom encourages senators to give careful thought to a bill. Sometimes, a long debate "talks a bill to death." This is called a **filibuster.** The senators can vote to stop the filibuster. This is called the **cloture rule** and requires a 3/5 vote of the Senate to end debate. However, more often than not, the vote fails. Then the bill cannot go forward.

Both the Senate and the House of Representatives must approve a bill before it can be sent to the President. Many times, the two houses have to **compromise** on a bill. The bicameral system allows for these compromises. Even if both houses do agree on a bill, the President has the power to **veto** (turn down) their legislation. It takes a 2/3 vote of both houses to **override** (go over) the President's veto.

In addition to making laws, the Senate has several other nonlegislative duties. The Senate approves or rejects presidential appointments, such as cabinet members and justices for the Supreme Court. It also approves or rejects treaties. Finally, the Senate judges impeachment cases brought against government officials by the House. A 2/3 vote is required for conviction.

UNIT 4

A Make a list of four important differences between the Senate and the House of Representatives.

1. ______________________________
2. ______________________________
3. ______________________________
4. ______________________________

B Fill in each blank with the correct term or number. Choose the answer from the word box.

Word Box

President	state	House of Representatives
2/3	veto	Vice President
Senate	six	filibuster
two	100	pro tempore

The Senate

The upper house of our Congress is called the ______________. There are ______________ members in the upper house. Only ______________ senators are elected in each ______________. They serve a term of ______________ years. The ______________ ______________ is the president of the Senate. In his or her absence the Senate has a president ______________ ______________. Sometimes senators try to talk a bill to death. This is called a ______________. Even if the Senate and the ______________ ______________ ______________ pass a bill, the ______________ can still ______________ it. It takes a ______________ vote to override the President's refusal to sign the bill.

Congressional Committees

Committees do most of the actual work of the House and Senate. Every party has members on these committees. There are four basic types of committees for both the Senate and the House: (1) **standing** (or permanent), (2) **select,** (3) **conference,** and (4) **joint.**

Standing committees are the most important type. They deal with bills concerning specific legislative subjects. The Senate has 16 standing committees, the most powerful of which are probably Appropriations, Armed Services, Judiciary, and Foreign Relations. The House has 22 standing committees, the most powerful of which are probably Appropriations, Judiciary, Rules, and Ways and Means.

Most standing committees are divided into subcommittees. The House has about 140 subcommittees.

Select committees, also called *special committees,* are temporary groups formed for investigations or other special purposes.

Conference committees and joint committees are made up of members of both houses of Congress. Conference committees resolve differences in bills that have passed both houses of Congress. Joint committees deal with topics that concern both houses, such as energy problems or economic matters.

Heads of committees and subcommittees are members of the majority party. Usually the person chosen is the one who has served the longest on that committee or subcommittee and is from the majority.

A List the four types of committees.

1. ______________________________
2. ______________________________
3. ______________________________
4. ______________________________

B Underline the correct answer.

1. The (standing, joint) committee is the most important kind of committee.
2. Most standing committees are divided into (houses, subcommittees).
3. (Select, Rules) committees conduct investigations.
4. Heads of committees are members of the (majority, minority) party.

UNIT 4

Review Unit 4

Read each puzzle clue. Then write the word being defined where it belongs in the puzzle.

The Congress

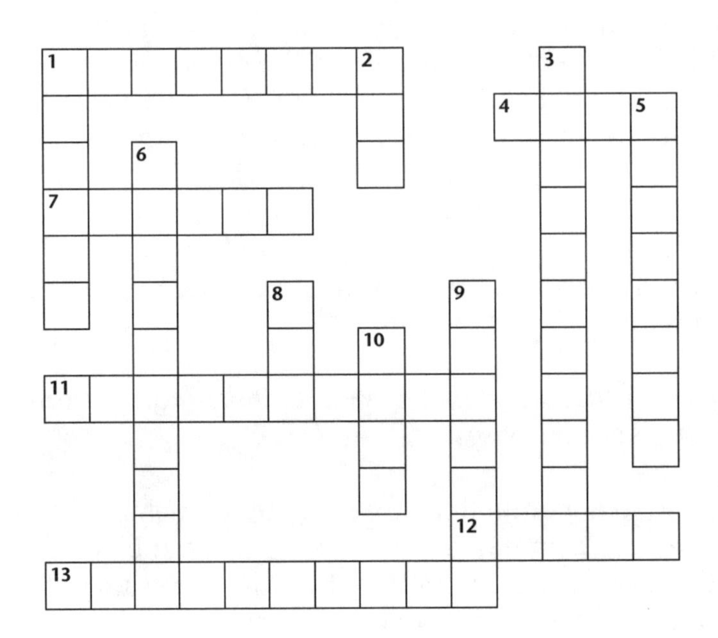

ACROSS

1. legislative branch of the United States government
4. time a person serves in Congress
7. the upper house of Congress
11. when each side gives in a little to reach an agreement
12. what Americans do to choose representatives
13. To "talk a bill to death" on the floor

DOWN

1. process of counting people every ten years
2. term of office, in years, for the Senate
3. lawmaking branch of government
5. over 50 percent
6. a one-house legislature
8. term of office, in years, for the House
9. leader of the House
10. future law

The President

The executive branch of the government is headed by the President of the United States. The President is the **chief executive officer** in charge of making sure the laws of the country are carried out, or **enforced.**

The American people elect the President **indirectly.** When they vote for President, they are really voting for members of the **electoral college.** The electoral college are people chosen from each state to cast votes for Presidents. Each state has the same number of **electors,** members of the electoral college, as they have senators and representatives. A state's electors most often vote for the person who received the most votes for President in the state.

To become President, a person must have specific qualifications.

The President must be—

- a natural-born citizen of the United States. When the Constitution was adopted, anyone who was a citizen of the United States could be President.
- at least 35 years old.
- a resident of the United States for 14 years

The President serves a term of four years. George Washington, our first President, served two terms and would not accept a third term. The custom (not law) became that a President served for only two terms. Franklin D. Roosevelt broke that custom in 1940 and 1944, when he was elected to a third and fourth term.

In 1951, the Twenty-second Amendment was added to the Constitution. This amendment states that a President of the United States may serve for only two terms and no more than ten years. A President who assumes office after a sitting President becomes sick, dies, resigns (quits), or is removed from office finishes out the term of office of the previous President. If the new President takes office after only one year into the previous President's term, he or she may serve as President for only one more term. This is because he or she would serve as President for three years of the previous President's term and four years for his or her own term. This equals seven years. Serving another term would take the number of years served up to 11, and the amendment says that the President cannot serve for more than ten years.

UNIT 5

A Fill in the blanks with the correct term or number. Choose the answer from the word box.

Word Box

two	1951	Franklin D. Roosevelt	elected
14	George Washington	Twenty-second	35
President	four	ten	citizen
electoral college	indirectly	chief executive officer	

The Executive Branch

The ________________ holds the highest position in the executive branch of our federal government. The President is the ________________ ________________ ________________ of the government. Americans ________________ elect the President. Members of the ________________ ________________ are chosen by the people, and these members elect the President. To be elected President, a person must be a natural-born ________________, at least ________________ years of age, and have lived in the United States for ________________ years. The term of office is ________________ years.

Earlier Presidents served no more than ________________ terms. That custom was established by our first President, ________________ ________________. The only President to serve more than two terms was ________________ ________________ ________________ He was ________________ four times. In the year ________________ the ________________ Amendment was passed. The amendment said that a President could serve only a total of ________________ years.

B Write your answers to the questions.

1. Who is the President today?________________
2. How many years has this President served? ________________
3. Will this President be able to serve another term? Why or why not?________________

____

4. **Special Thought Question:** There should be no limit to the number of terms a President can serve. Do you agree or disagree? Why?

____

____

The Vice President

In the early presidential elections, the person who received the most electoral votes became President, and the person who received the second highest number of electoral votes automatically became the Vice President. This system ran into a problem in the elections of 1796 and 1800. In 1796, John Adams, a Federalist, received the most electoral votes and became President. Thomas Jefferson, a Democratic-Republican, received the second highest number of votes and became Vice President. Being from different political parties, the President and Vice President had very different ideas about how the government should work. This caused problems as they opposed one another.

Then in 1800, Thomas Jefferson and Aaron Burr, both Democratic-Republicans, ended up in a tie. The House of Representatives had to decide who the winner should be. Finally, they declared Thomas Jefferson the winner, and he became the President. Burr became Vice President.

The Twelfth Amendment was added in 1804 to change the election process so that electors voted for the President and the Vice President on separate ballots. In present-day elections, the President and Vice President run together. If the presidential candidate of a party wins, the vice presidential candidate also wins.

The same qualifications for office that apply to the President also apply to the Vice President. The term of office is the same. Even though the position of Vice President is of great importance, it has often been taken for granted and described by some as a "do-nothing job."

The Importance of the Vice President

The Vice President serves as the presiding officer of the Senate and has the title of president of the United States Senate. The Constitution gives the Vice President no other official duties. The president of the Senate is like a chairperson. The Vice President cannot take part in debates, nor can the Vice President vote except in the rare event of a tie. Usually, the *majority party* leader and the *minority party* leader take care of most of the business of the Senate. The Vice President has other duties and cannot always be present when the Senate meets.

The role and importance of the Vice President has gradually been increasing. Since the presidency of Franklin Roosevelt, Vice Presidents have regularly attended cabinet meetings. Today, the Vice President helps the President by attending social and political events. Often the Vice President travels to other countries to speak on behalf of the President.

The office of Vice President has always been a very special position. The choice of a Vice President should be given serious thought. It has been said that the Vice President is only a heartbeat away from being President, the most powerful elective office in the world. The Vice President has taken over the office of the

U N I T 5

President nine times in our country's history. The chart on this page shows when this happened.

The Twenty-fifth Amendment, which was added in 1967, spells out what happens when a President becomes disabled and the Vice President must take over. The amendment also spells out what happens if the office of Vice President becomes vacant. Then the President appoints a new Vice President. The appointment must be approved by the majority of both houses of Congress. In 1973, House minority leader Gerald Ford became the first Vice President chosen under the terms of the Twenty-fifth Amendment. Ford succeeded Spiro Agnew who had resigned as Vice President.

Vice Presidents Who Succeeded to the Presidency	
John Tyler	upon the death (by pneumonia) of William Henry Harrison, April 14, 1841
Millard Fillmore	upon the death (by gastroenteritis) of Zachary Taylor, July 9, 1850
Andrew Johnson	upon the death (by **assassination**) of Abraham Lincoln, April 15, 1865
Chester A. Arthur	upon the death (by assassination) of James A. Garfield, September 19, 1881
Theodore Roosevelt	upon death (by assassination) of William McKinley, September 14, 1901
Calvin Coolidge	upon the death (by stroke) of Warren G. Harding, August 2, 1923
Harry S. Truman	upon the death (by cerebral hemorrhage) of Franklin D. Roosevelt, April 12, 1945
Lyndon B. Johnson	upon the death (by assassination) of John F. Kennedy, November 22, 1963
Gerald Ford	upon the resignation of Richard M. Nixon, August 9, 1974

UNIT 5

A Write a brief paragraph in which you explain why the Twelfth Amendment was added to our Constitution.

____
____
____
____
____

B Answer the questions below.

1. Why must the qualifications of the office of Vice President be exactly the same as those of the President?

____
____

2. What position does the Vice President hold in the Senate? ______________________

3. How does the Vice President help the President? ______________________

____
____

4. Why has the office of the Vice President always been an important one?

____
____

5. How many times has the Vice President been called upon to replace the President? _____

   How many Presidents died in office? _____

   How many were assassinated (killed)? _____

   How many resigned (quit)? _____

6. **Special Thought Question:** Should the Vice President be given more power as an elected official of our government?

____
____
____

Duties of the President

The President has many important jobs to do. How well the President does the job will affect the success of the President's party in future elections. The President is the country's highest elected official. Many **departments** have been organized to help the President enforce the laws.

During the election proceedings, the presidential candidate talks about the changes he or she would like to make. The President cannot make these changes alone. The President works with Congress to get new laws passed and changes made.

The Constitution makes the President **commander in chief** of the armed forces. That means all military officials must obey the President. However, the President does not have the power to declare war; only Congress can do that. The President can, however, issue orders that require the use of the armed forces in a time of emergency.

The President is the leader in **foreign policy.** Foreign policy includes such things as **treaties,** agreements, peace talks, and economic (business) affairs with other countries. The President can make treaties with other nations, but Senate approval of a treaty is needed before it can become law.

The Constitution also requires the President to provide information about the state of the Union, or how things are going in the country. The President provides such information to the Congress in his annual State of the Union Address, which is given in January. Today the address is broadcast so that all the people in the nation may see and hear the President's presentation.

The President is the **ceremonial** leader of the country. The President is asked to visit other countries as a friend and also invites other world leaders to visit the United States. In this way, people from different countries can learn to understand each other better.

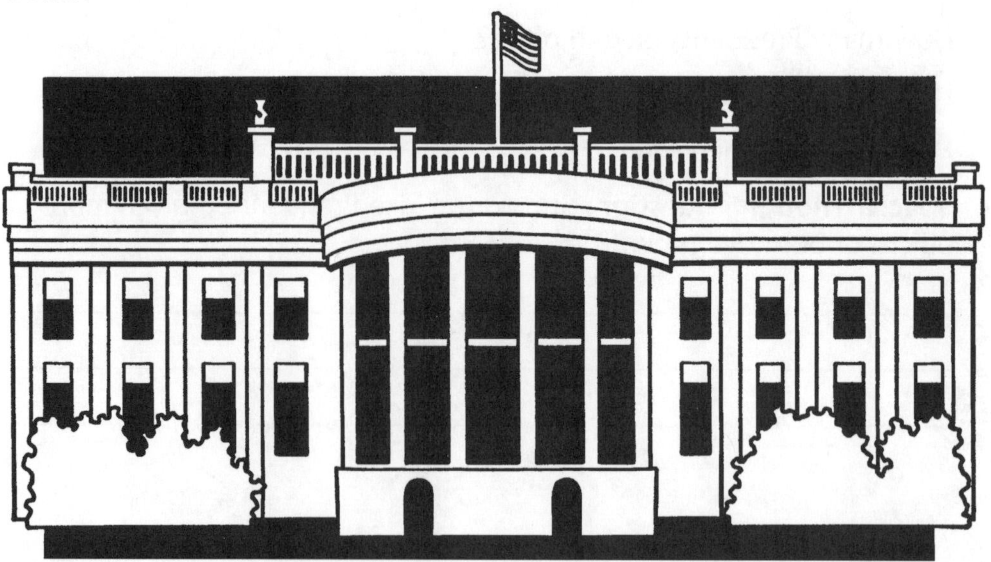

The White House is the official residence of the President. It is located at 1600 Pennsylvania Avenue in Washington, D.C.

UNIT 5

A The President of the United States has several important duties. List six.

1. ______________________
2. ______________________
3. ______________________
4. ______________________
5. ______________________
6. ______________________

B Write your answer to the question.

Special Thought Question: *Civilian* means a person not in any of the armed forces. Why is it so important to our democracy that the President, a civilian, is the commander in chief of the armed forces?

____

____

____

____

____

____

____

C Write *True* or *False* on the line in front of each statement.

__________ 1. One of the main duties of the President is to enforce the laws that have been enacted.

__________ 2. The President establishes what our policies toward other countries will be and how we will act toward them.

__________ 3. The President's performance has little effect on his political party's future.

__________ 4. The President can influence Congress by asking the members to pass certain bills.

__________ 5. To declare war, the President makes an announcement to Congress.

The Cabinet

In 1789, George Washington became the first President of the new country. The Constitution was in effect and was the supreme law of the land. President Washington decided that he needed knowledgeable people to help him make important decisions. He selected four people to be his special advisers. These people were called his **cabinet.** The Constitution of the United States makes no mention of a cabinet. However, in 1789, Congress established three departments—State, War, and Treasury—plus the office of Attorney General. The first recorded cabinet meeting was held in 1791. Thomas Jefferson became the secretary of state; Alexander Hamilton, the secretary of the treasury; Henry Knox, the secretary of war; and Edmund Randolph, the attorney general.

As time passed, more departments were added. At present, there are 14 departments. Each cabinet member has the title of secretary. The departments are State, Treasury, Defense, Justice, Interior, Commerce, Labor, Agriculture, Housing and Urban Development, Transportation, Energy, Health and Human Services, Veterans Affairs, and Education. Each cabinet member is an expert in his or her field. The departments that the secretaries head up employ many people. It is very important that each department does a good job. From time to time, Presidents have asked other officials in the executive branch to take part in cabinet meetings regularly. In general, membership in the cabinet is determined by the President.

The President appoints the cabinet, but the appointments must be approved by the Senate. The President may dismiss a cabinet member at any time. By custom, the cabinet resigns when a new President takes office.

The President meets with the cabinet regularly to discuss important issues facing the country. The President is usually the one who calls the cabinet meetings, which usually take place weekly in the Cabinet Room of the White House. During these meetings, suggestions for action, new laws, and changes are made to the President. All final decisions, however, are the responsibility of the President.

The President also has other helpers. The White House staff takes care of any routine (regular) business. Staff workers take care of phone calls, schedule appointments, and arrange for visitors. Other White House staff members organize and arrange special events, make travel arrangements for the President, and meet with the news reporters who cover the White House. The job of the White House staff is to allow the President to make the best use of every busy day.

Review Unit 5

A Complete the following exercise by filling in the blanks. Use the words listed below.

Word Box

decisions	experts
14	departments
war	state
attorney general	cabinet
George Washington	four
President	first
treasury	

The Cabinet

In 1789, ____________ ____________ became the ____________ President of the United States. He chose ____________ advisers to help him. That was the beginning of the first ____________. The advisers were the secretaries of ____________, ____________, and ____________, and the ____________ ____________.

As time passed, more ____________ were added. There are now ____________ advisers to the ____________. The advisers are ____________ in their fields. They meet with the President and make suggestions. The final ____________ are made by the President.

B Write a brief paragraph in which you summarize how the White House staff helps the President.

____

____

____

____

____

____

UNIT 5

C Write your answers to the questions.

Forming an Opinion

1. Former President Jimmy Carter suggested one term of six years for the President. Do you agree or disagree with this proposal? Why or why not?

2. If the President is unable to finish his or her term, regardless of the reason, a new election should be held. Do you agree or disagree? Why or why not?

3. If you were able to vote for the President, what would you want him or her to be like?

4. What are three key issues or problems that you would like to see the President deal with?

UNIT 5

5. The United States has never had a woman President. Many women are well qualified. Do you think it is possible that we will have a woman President soon? Explain.

6. The United States has never had a member of a minority group as President. Many are well qualified. Do you think it is possible that we will have a minority President soon? Explain.

7. An age limit of 35 has been set as the youngest a person can be to run for the presidency. Why not have an age limit for the oldest a person can be?

8. Cabinet members are selected by the President and approved by the Senate. Would it be better to elect cabinet members as we do the President? What do you think?

9. It has been suggested that there are too many government departments and that some, such as the departments of Transportation, Commerce, and Education, should be eliminated. Do you think some departments should be cut? What might be some advantages? What might be some disadvantages?

10. The election process for President includes a long primary campaign and a long election campaign. Some think there should be a one-day primary when the entire country votes for the presidential candidate for their chosen party. What do you think of this idea? What are some of the advantages and disadvantages?

11. The President has the power to veto bills. What do you think are some reasons a President might do this?

The Courts and the Constitution

The federal courts and the state courts are important to a democratic system. People expect the court systems to be fair and equal for all Americans. They expect judges to know the laws and make responsible decisions. The judicial branch is the cornerstone of liberty, justice, and equality under the Constitution. The judicial branch of government is responsible for **interpreting,** or explaining the meaning of, the laws. The Constitution established only one court, the **Supreme Court.** Congress established all of the lower federal courts.

Supreme Court—The Judicial Branch

The Supreme Court is the highest court in the United States. It is the only court that has the power to declare a law **unconstitutional,** or against what the Constitution says. This is called the power of **judicial review.** The Constitution did not state that the Supreme Court had the power of judicial review. This power arose from a case brought to the Supreme Court in the early 1800s. In the *Marbury vs. Madison* case, Marbury asked the Court to force Madison, the secretary of state, to recognize Marbury's appointment to an office. According to the Judiciary Act, the Supreme Court had jurisdiction over the decision. The Court decided that it did not have power to make the decision because the Judiciary Act was unconstitutional. Ever since this case, the Supreme Court has used the power of judicial review.

The Supreme Court differs from the lower courts in several ways. It can hear the original cases in only a small number of cases. These are cases affecting ambassadors, consuls, and two or more states. The Supreme Court is, however, the highest court of **appeal.** It does not actually try appeal cases. It only reviews cases that have already been tried in the lower courts. Many times an appeal is returned to the lower court because the Supreme Court does not think it was significant enough for their attention.

The Supreme Court does not give a verdict of guilty or innocent in appeal cases. Instead, the court gives an **opinion** or a decision. The Supreme Court's decision is final on any questions about federal law.

Choosing the Members of the Court

Presently the Supreme Court has nine members. Eight of the members are called **associate justices** and one is called the **chief justice.** The justices are all equal. However, the chief justice is considered to be the leader of the court. The court has had nine members for over 100 years.

An associate justice is appointed to the court by the President. The Senate has the power to refuse the person recommended by the President. When this happens, the President must recommend someone else. The Senate looks into the background of all potential Supreme Court members. Once the associate justice has been approved, he or she will serve for life, and Congress cannot reduce his or her salary. These provisions protect the justices from political control and ensure their independence. The appointment, therefore, requires very serious thought. A justice can be removed after impeachment and trial for corruption or other abuses in office, but this has never occurred.

The Court meets regularly in the Supreme Court Building in Washington, D. C. The annual term of the Court begins on the first Monday in October and usually ends in June.

The justices decide a case after they have considered oral and written arguments from each side. During oral arguments, the justices are free to ask questions. After oral arguments, the justices discuss the case in conference (in private). After the discussion, a vote is taken. Cases are decided by a majority vote. If a tie occurs, the lower court decision is left standing. The parties in the case have no further appeal.

One of the justices who voted in the majority is assigned to write the majority opinion. Those who voted in the minority may write a dissenting opinion stating why they disagreed. Justices may also write a concurring opinion if they agree with the majority but not for the reasons given in the majority opinion or if they wish to express similar reasons in their own words.

The Supreme Court is the highest level in the court system of the United States.

A Underline the correct answer.

1. There are (15, 9) members of the Supreme Court.
2. The President recommends a justice to the Supreme Court. Only the (Senate, House of Representatives) can refuse a recommendation.
3. Supreme Court justices serve a term of (20 years, life).
4. The Supreme Court was created by the (Constitution, Congress).
5. The head of the Supreme Court is called the (associate, chief) justice.

B Fill in the blanks with the correct term. Choose the answer from the word box.

Word Box	
Supreme	Congress
unconstitutional	Constitution
laws	opinions

1. The judicial branch interprets (explains) the ____________________.
2. The highest court in the judicial branch is the ____________________ Court.
3. All of the other federal courts of our judicial system were made by the ____________________.
4. When a law goes against the Constitution, it is said to be ____________________.
5. The supreme law of the United States is the ____________________.
6. The Supreme Court does not try cases of appeal; it gives ____________________.

How the Supreme Court Works

The Supreme Court has eight associate justices and a chief justice. When a case is reviewed, the justices listen to the facts that are presented by attorneys. The justices also ask questions so that they understand all of the important details of the case. They study the case and read to gather additional information. This step can take weeks, maybe months.

Usually a majority of five votes is needed to change the lower court's original decision. However, in all rulings, six justices must be present when a decision is given. Four of those six must agree on the decision. A tie vote is the same as saying that a change in the lower court's decision is not necessary. The court does not issue a verdict of guilt or innocence. The justices *interpret* the meaning of the Constitution and give their opinions **(ruling).** The ruling is important because it affects the previous decision of the lower courts. For example, a person's **constitutional rights** might have been denied (not given) him or her.

The Supreme Court's opinion may mean a new trial is required. Or, the ruling could **uphold,** or agree with, the decision of the lower courts. Only the most important cases are heard by the Supreme Court.

■ List nine facts about the Supreme Court.

1. ______________________________
2. ______________________________
3. ______________________________
4. ______________________________
5. ______________________________
6. ______________________________
7. ______________________________
8. ______________________________
9. ______________________________

The Lower Courts

The Supreme Court is the highest court in the United States. There are, however, a number of other federal courts. Tax courts, military courts, customs courts, and district courts are just a few. Federal courts deal with cases that involve the federal government in some way. Bank robbery, kidnapping, mail fraud, treason, and tax problems are examples of cases that would be tried in the federal courts.

State Courts

Each state has the power to organize its own court system. The courts are arranged depending upon the legislature of each state. States have different levels of courts and different names.

Judges in the state courts perform many of the same duties as federal judges. They may be selected in different ways, however. In many states, judges are elected. In others, they are appointed by elected officials and then confirmed or rejected by the people during an election. In still other states, the judges are appointed. The term of office of a state judge varies from state to state and by level of the court on which the judge serves.

Those in charge of the lowest courts are known as justices of the peace. "JP's," as they are called, hear minor **civil** (noncriminal) cases or **misdemeanors** (less serious crimes).

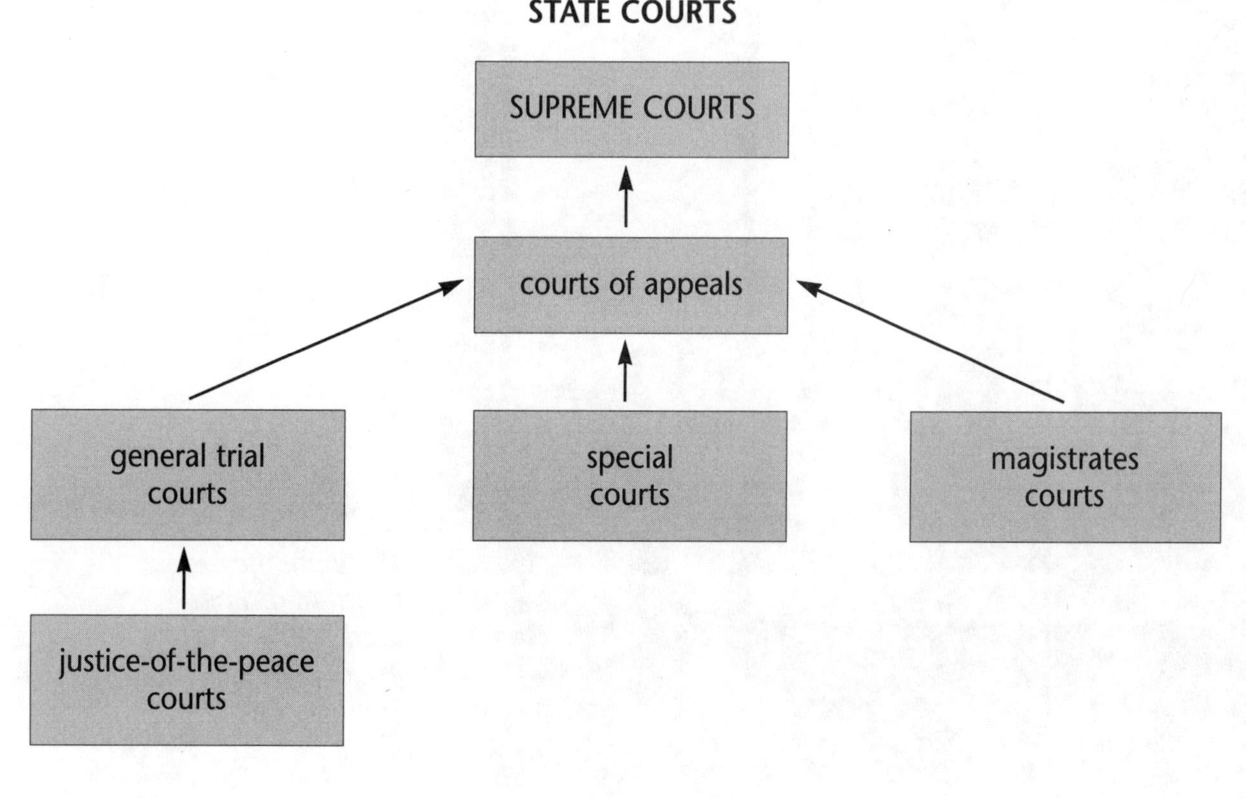

Magistrate courts are similar to justice courts and are found in cities. These courts are run by magistrates. The cases brought before the magistrate courts are misdemeanors and minor civil cases.

The more serious crimes, called **felonies,** and civil cases are heard by judges in the trial courts. The trial courts use the jury system. A jury is a group of people who listens to all the facts and then give a **verdict,** or decision. States are divided into districts, or **circuits,** to take care of cases throughout the entire state.

Most of the states call their highest court, the state supreme court. Sometimes other names are used. The state supreme court works very much like the federal Supreme Court. Its member judges are called *justices,* just as the federal Supreme Court members are. An appeal to the highest court in the state can be made to review a lower court's decision. If the state supreme court does review the decision, it does so because there is some question of improper (wrong) treatment of the case. The state supreme court's decision is usually final. It is possible, but not likely, that the problem would be reviewed by the federal Supreme Court.

These are the bench and chairs used by the nine justices of the Supreme Court.

Review Unit 6

A Write one fact about each of the following:

1. justices of the peace ______________________________

2. magistrate courts ______________________________

3. general trial courts ______________________________

4. state supreme court ______________________________

5. circuits ______________________________

6. civil cases ______________________________

B The federal Supreme Court and the state supreme courts are very much alike. Write a brief paragraph in which you summarize how they are similar.

____

C Underline the correct answer.

1. A jury listens to evidence and then gives (an interpretation, a verdict).
2. More serious crimes are called (felonies, misdemeanors).
3. Two types of cases are criminal and (public, civil) cases.

REVIEW

Review Units 4–6

Write the word from the box that completes each sentence.

Word Box

verdicts	four	secretaries
cabinet	Congress	nine
Senate	opinions	trade
court	civil	bicameral

1. The legislative branch of government is called ______________________.
2. A two-house legislature is called ______________________.
3. Congress is made up of the House of Representatives and the ______________________.
4. Congress has the power to regulate ______________________ between states.
5. The President is elected for a term of ______________________ years.
6. The President has a ______________________ that advises him on matters related to government departments.
7. Heads of the executive departments are called ______________________.
8. There are ______________________ members on the Supreme Court.
9. The Supreme Court issues ______________________.
10. States have their own ______________________ system.
11. Juries listen to cases and come up with ______________________.
12. Magistrate courts hear minor ______________________ cases.

State Government

The federal system of government shares power between the central government and the state government. This is called **limited government.** The Constitution limits the power of the central government. The writers of the Constitution were concerned that the states would be powerless and controlled by the central government. James Madison warned of the dangers of too much power in the hands of a few people.

The issue of states' rights has always been a controversial one. Leaders such as Madison and Jefferson believed states had a right to judge whether Congress went beyond its constitutional powers. They believed the states should keep most of the power. Others warned that this view could destroy the Constitution. They believed that a strong national government was needed to handle the issues facing the country.

The Constitution of the United States recognizes state governments, but it does not list the powers that belong to the states. It does identify some things states cannot do, such as make treaties. The Tenth Amendment, however, says that the powers not given to the national government or denied to the states belong to the states or the people.

State government is unitary. This means that no county or city governments are required. Some countries are completely unitary and do not even have state governments. That is why the federal system is so unusual. For example, as mentioned before, the United Kingdom has a unitary system. There, other units of government are organized and permitted only for the convenience of the central, or national, government.

In order to become a state, each of the thirteen original colonies had to have a Constitution. The state laws, rights, and regulations had to agree with the federal Constitution. Each of the fifty states has its own Constitution. If other areas become states, such as the District of Columbia and Puerto Rico, they, too, will need to have their own Constitutions. Over the years, some states have written and adopted new constitutions. Wisconsin, for example, adopted a new constitution in 1970. Other states have had the same constitution since they became states. Maine, for example, has had the same Constitution since it became a state in 1820. It, like other states, usually amends its constitution to meet changing needs.

States can **levy** taxes, have courts of law, build roads, organize schools, and do many more things that are important in the daily lives of the residents. In some cases, state constitutions are much longer and more detailed than the national constitution.

U N I T 7

Complete the following exercise. Use complete sentences when writing your answers.

1. When our country first began, how many states did we have? ______

2. Why did each state need to write its own constitution? ______

3. Would it be possible for more states to be added in the future? ______

4. States have the power to
   a. ______
   b. ______
   c. ______
   d. ______

5. Write two facts about state constitutions. ______

6. Write two facts about our federal Constitution. ______

7. Name two early supporters of states' rights. ______

8. What do people who believe in states' rights think? ______

9. What do those who favor a strong central government think about the states' rights argument? ______

10. What does it mean to say that a state government is unitary? ______

Organization of State Government

The thirteen original states had constitutions before the United States Constitution was written. Some of them were used for ideas in the United States Constitution. Since then, the state governments have followed the model of the federal government. The two-house (bicameral) system of the federal government was adopted by all of the states. In 1934, Nebraska, however, decided to have only one house. This type of organization is called *unicameral.* The states have a lawmaking branch exactly like the federal government. In most states, the two houses are called the *senate* and the *house,* just as in the federal government. Members of the legislative branch are concerned about the people they represent.

As described in a previous unit, states also have a judicial branch, with their own system of courts.

The Governor

As in the federal government, states also have an executive branch. The most important elected official in state government is the **governor**, who is the head of the executive branch. The following qualifications are needed for a person to serve as governor of a state:

- must be an American citizen.
- must be of a certain age (usually 25 or 30).
- have lived in the state for a certain period of time (usually five years).
- must be a qualified voter.

The governor has powers very similar to those of the President of the United States. He or she is the chief executive of the state. Like the President, governors cannot make laws. They can only suggest laws and changes that might be needed. Too, in all states except North Carolina, the governor may veto a bill. Like the President's annual State of the Union Address, a governor also makes a yearly speech called the *State of the State Address.*

The governor plays a major role in running the state. He or she represents the whole state, not just big cities or small towns. The governor needs cooperation and support from all parts of the state. This is a challenging job especially in states that have very large populations. For example, California has more people than the entire country of Canada. New York state has more people than Norway and Sweden combined.

Governors are also seen as the heads of their political party in the state. Their effectiveness as governor can affect the success or failure of their political party in the state and can have an influence on national elections for congressional offices and for the presidency.

U
N

T
7

Because the role of governor is important and requires leadership, some governors go on to the Congress of the United States. Some have been elected President. Three recent examples of state governors who later became President are Jimmy Carter of Georgia, Ronald Reagan of California, and Bill Clinton of Arkansas.

A Complete the following exercise by filling in the blanks. Use the words listed below.

Word Box					
Nebraska	bicameral	unicameral	two	legislative	state

State Government

The federal government has served as a model for ____________________ governments. The ____________________ branch in most states has ____________________ houses. This is called a ____________________ system. All of the states except ____________________ have two houses. A one-house state government is called ____________________.

B Write your answers to the activities that follow.

1. What is the title given to the chief executive of a state government?

   ____

2. List three qualifications required to be the chief executive of a state.

   a. ____

   b. ____

   c. ____

C Complete the following exercises. Use complete sentences in writing your answers.

1. Why is the governor's job important to the state? ____________________________________

   ____

2. How is a governor's job like that of the President? How does it differ?

   ____

   ____

The State Legislative Branch

Most of the fifty states have an annual (yearly) legislative session. The session is held in their state capitals. The length of each session varies from state to state. Some states allow five to six months for a legislative session, while others have only thirty days. In recent years, the trend has been to increase the length of time needed to take care of the state's business.

A person must be an American **citizen** and a legal resident of the state and must also live in the district he or she represents to serve in the state legislature. Usually, a senator must be at least 25 years of age. Representatives or delegates usually must be at least 21 years of age.

The names of the state legislative bodies may also be different. Most states simply call it the legislature. Some states, such as Maryland, call it the general assembly. Other names used are legislative assembly and general court. Regardless of the name used, the legislative bodies work very much the same way. Nebraska is different from the other states because it has only one house.

The names of the legislative chambers (houses) of states can also be different. The upper house is called the *senate.* State senates are patterned after the United States Senate. Most states refer to the larger lower house as the house of representatives. Three states call it the house of delegates, and five states refer to it as the assembly.

Usually, the term of office for a state senator is four years. The term of office for a state representative or delegate, in a majority of states, is two years.

TYPICAL STRUCTURE OF A STATE LEGISLATURE

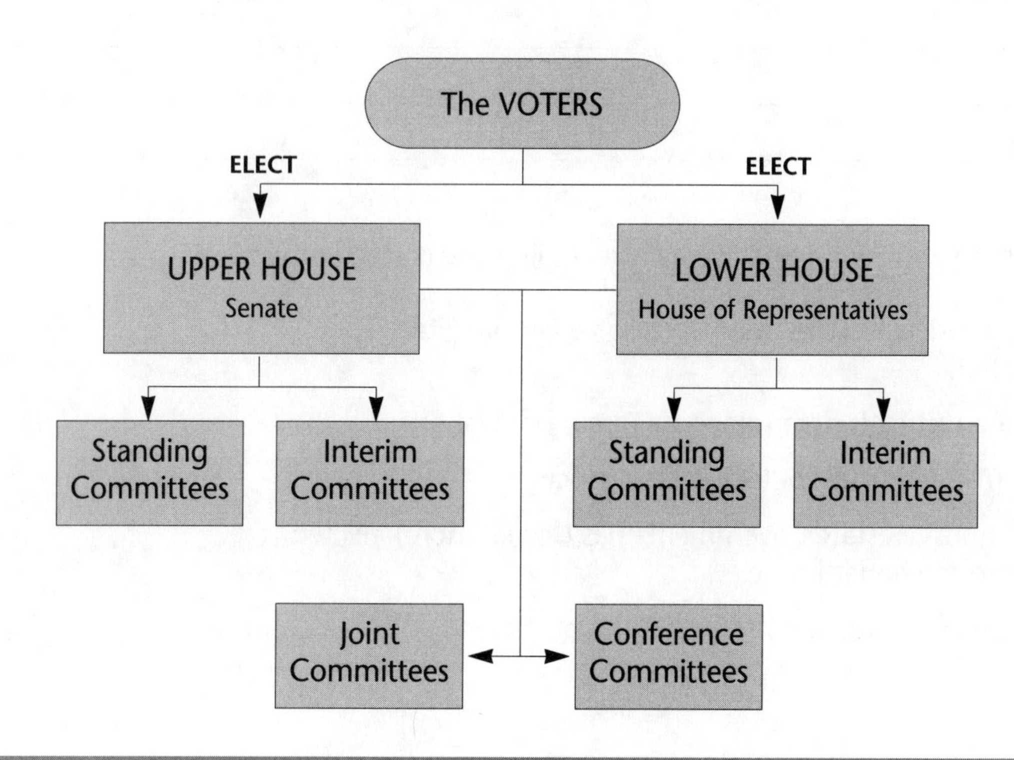

UNIT 7

Legislative Districts

Legislative districts were established in order to give people equal representation. The size of each district is determined by population. Each district must be equal in size in terms of population. Each state decides the number of the districts it will have.

There are two sets of districts, one for the lower house and one for the upper house. It is necessary to have two sets of districts because the lower house has more members than the upper house. The voter will choose one representative for each house from each district.

A List three requirements that a person must meet to be elected to a state legislature.

1. ____________________
2. ____________________
3. ____________________

B The names of state legislatures are not the same in all of the states. List four names used. What is the name used in your state?

1. ____________________
2. ____________________
3. ____________________
4. ____________________
5. Your state____________________

C Complete the following exercise by underlining the correct answer.

1. Legislative districts were established to give people (little, equal) representation.
2. The size of a district is determined by (area, population).
3. There are (five, two) sets of legislative districts.
4. The lower house in state governments has (fewer, more) elected officials than the upper house.
5. The Montana state legislature is (unicameral, bicameral).

How the Legislature Works

All states, except Nebraska, have two houses. The lower house has more members than the upper house. The majority party in each house chooses a leader for both houses. In the lower house, the leader is called the **speaker.** In the upper house, some states call the leader the **lieutenant governor.** In states without a lieutenant governor, a leader is chosen from the majority party.

The leaders of the upper and lower houses have very important positions. They have the power to organize the committees and set the schedule of daily business. They also decide which bills will be discussed. The leaders must be able to get the members to work together. The success or failure of the state legislature depends upon cooperation among the leaders and the governor.

Many state governments, like the United States government, have a system of check and balances. In a number of states, the legislatures approve or reject officials appointed by the governor. They approve the state budget. Except for the Oregon legislature, state legislatures can impeach and determine the innocence or guilt of state government officials.

■ Fill in each blank with the correct term. Choose the answer from the word box. You will not use all the words.

Word Box

daily	governor	committees
lieutenant	upper	majority
speaker	bills	lower

How the Legislature Works

The ____________________ (leader) of the lower house is chosen by the ____________________ party. In states that have a ____________________ governor, he or she often serves as the leader in the ____________________ house. The leaders of the state legislatures have the power to organize ____________________ and set the ____________________ schedule of business. The leaders must also be able to work together with other members and the ____________________.

State Government Today

State governments have a lot of work to do. Most of the states have annual legislative sessions. The length of time for these sessions is different in each state. The state governments need to deal with many problems and issues. Issues such as housing, public transportation, conservation, prisons, public health, and education programs affect the citizens of the states.

State-run programs are very expensive, and the costs continue to rise. They are paid for by taxes collected by the state. States collect such taxes as income tax, sales tax, and motor fuel tax. Some receive income from state lotteries. Some of a state's money comes from the federal government in the form of **grants in aid.**

The local governments of cities, towns, and other communities also need money to run properly. They use the money to provide police and fire services, maintain local streets, and provide many other services to community residents. They receive income from such sources as property taxes, utility taxes, and licenses and fees. They also receive grants in aid from their state.

Decide whether each statement is *True* or *False.* Write the correct answer in the space provided.

_______________ **1.** Most states have yearly legislative sessions.

_______________ **2.** In recent years, the cost of state government has increased.

_______________ **3.** Grants in aid is one way the federal government helps the states.

_______________ **4.** State governments are very important in meeting the needs of the people.

_______________ **5.** States are not allowed to levy taxes.

_______________ **6.** States give some money to local communities.

_______________ **7.** Conservation and public transportation are funded by the federal government but not the state government.

_______________ **8.** Some state taxes might be used to build prisons and roads.

_______________ **9.** The legislative sessions are the same length of time in all the states.

_______________ **10.** States provide money for schools.

Review Unit 7

A Write the word from the word box that completes each sentence.

	Word Box	
bicameral	constitution	Oregon
three	unitary	Nebraska
governor	session	

1. States have ____________________ branches of government, just as the federal government does.
2. State government is a ____________________ form of government.
3. Each state has a ____________________ that must agrees with the one adopted by the United States.
4. Most state legislatures are ____________________.
5. The only state legislature that does not have impeachment power is ____________________.
6. Each state has an annual legislative ____________________.
7. The only state with a unicameral legislature is ____________________.
8. The most important elected official in a state is the

   ____________________.

B Write your answers to these questions.

1. What are two important problems facing the people in your state?

   a. ____

   b. ____

2. How might the problems be solved?

   a. ____

   b. ____

UNIT 7

C **For You to Investigate:** Look through encyclopedias, history books, and books about your state to find answers to the questions that follow.

1. What is the name of your state? ______________________________

2. What is the capital of your state? ______________________________

3. What is the name of the state legislature?______________________________

4. How many houses does the state legislature have?______________________________

5. What is each house called? ______________________________

6. How many members serve in the state senate? ______________________________

7. What is the term of office for your state senate? ______________________________

8. How many members serve in the lower house if your state has one? ______________________________

9. What is the term of office for members of the lower house?______________________________

10. When does your legislature meet? ______________________________

11. For how many days or months does it meet? ______________________________

12. Where does your legislature meet?______________________________

13. Does your state have a lieutenant governor? ______________________________

14. What is the name of the lieutenant governor?______________________________

15. Who is the governor of your state? ______________________________

16. When was your governor elected? ______________________________

17. Which political party does your governor represent? ______________________________

18. What is the term of office of your governor? ______________________________

19. Who is your state representative? ______________________________

20. Which political party does he or she represent?______________________________

21. Who is your state senator? ______________________________

22. Which political party does he or she represent?______________________________

Local Government Organization

The Constitution established a separation of powers between the federal government and state government. The Constitution, however, does not require the state government to set up local governments. State government is unitary. A unitary system of government is one in which no smaller units of government are required. If that is the case, why are there so many local units of government?

Communities grew in size as the United States increased in population. People moved from **rural** areas to **urban** communities. This trend established a need for more local government. Schools, law enforcement, public health, roads, traffic, and public services are some of the needs that are important to people in all communities. Local governments can respond more quickly to problems than state governments. In addition, people are more likely to know their local officials. When problems arise, people can go directly to these officials for help. Often the officials are friends or people who live in the neighborhood. This is democracy at its most basic level.

Today, most of the people in the United States live in villages, towns, and cities. Villages are the smallest communities. The population varies from only a few hundred people to several thousand. Towns are generally larger than villages. Cities are usually the largest of urban areas. Counties, parishes (in Louisiana), or boroughs (in Alaska) are the largest units of local government in a state. These units are different in name only. They all perform the same functions. These larger units of local government are especially important in rural areas where the people are widely scattered.

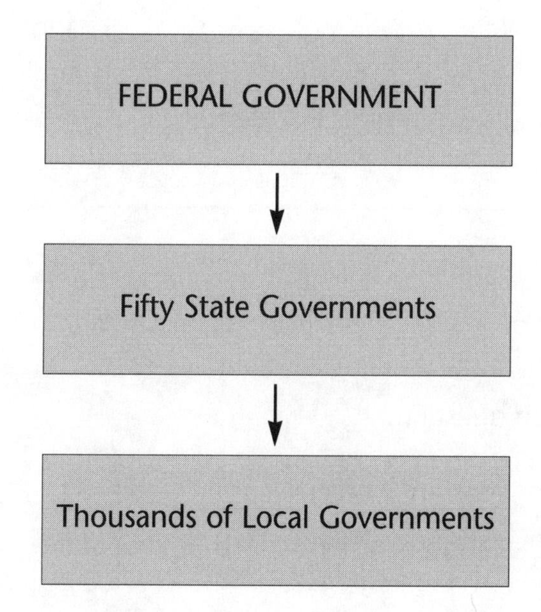

In the United States, there are three levels of governments.

UNIT 8

A Fill in the blanks with the correct term. Choose the answer from the word box.

Word Box		
rural	villages	separation of powers
parishes	boroughs	counties
share	unitary	cities
local	towns	state

Local Government

The Constitution of our country establishes a __________ ______ __________ between the federal government and __________ government. The states, however, do not have to set up any __________ governments. State governments are __________ and do not need to __________ power within the state. Nearly all of the fifty states are divided into __________, __________, or __________. County governments are important in __________ areas where people are widely scattered. Smaller units of local government may be found in __________, __________, and __________.

B List three reasons why local government is important.

1. ______________________________
2. ______________________________
3. ______________________________

C Write your answer to each question.

1. What is the name of one of your local officials? ______________________________
2. What is the largest unit of local government called in your state? ______________________________

States and Counties

Lesson 2

UNIT 8

There are many subdivisions of state government in the United States. For uniformity purposes, reference will be made to these subdivisions as counties throughout the text. At first, states divided into counties to serve the needs of the rural population. Over time, cities and towns grew larger. Many activities of the county are conducted at an urban county seat. This arrangement provides easy access for most of the people in the county.

The size of the state does not necessarily determine the number of counties. Some counties have large populations, while others have small populations. Counties take care of the special needs that people have.

County Government

The people who live in a county, but not in an organized town or city, need some type of government. The people of the county elect officials, usually called **commissioners.** The number of commissioners can vary from three to seven. The commissioners levy taxes, set up a budget, provide for education, and supervise road building, as well as a variety of other services.

In several states, a **board of supervisors** run the county government. The number of supervisors can vary from twelve to over fifty. Committees are set up to do much of the work.

Some county governments have an elected county executive. The county executive is like a mayor and is responsible for everything in the county government.

North Dakota

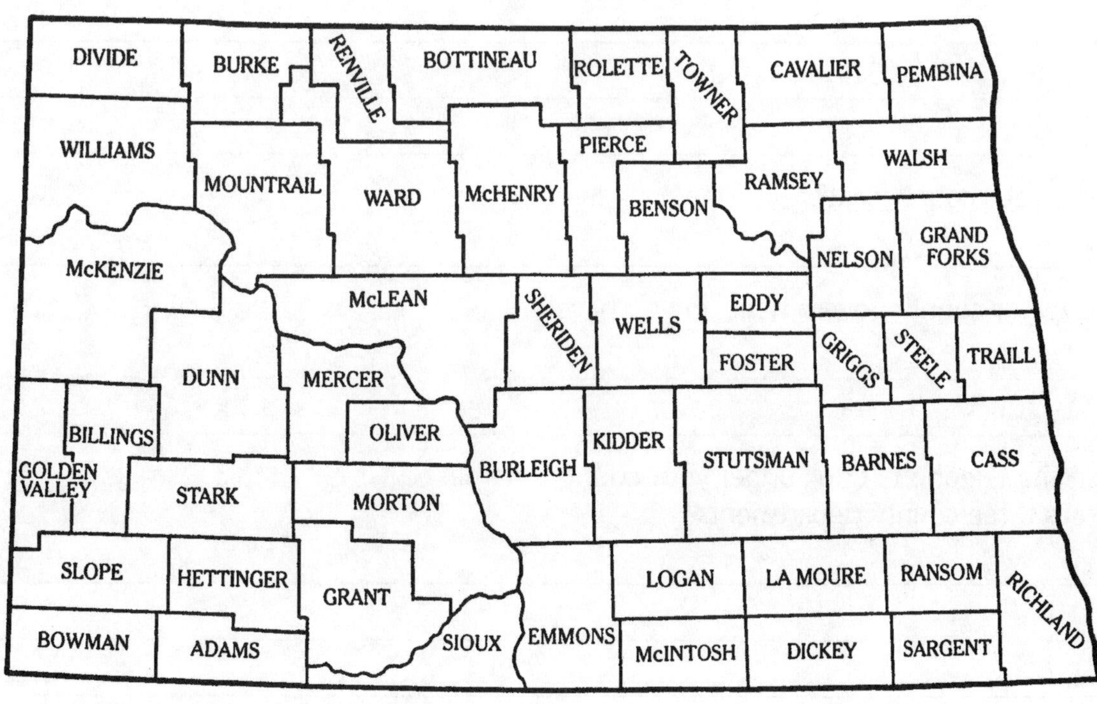

North Dakota is divided into many counties.

Answer each of the following questions in complete sentences.

1. Why are nearly all of the states divided into counties, parishes, or boroughs?

____

____

____

2. What are the two types of county governments?

a. ______________________________

b. ______________________________

3. Even though most of the people of a particular county are in urban areas, why is county government necessary?

____

____

____

____

4. What are some of the important jobs that county governments do? List four.

a. ______________________________

b. ______________________________

c. ______________________________

d. ______________________________

5. Where is your county seat?

____

6. What type of county government do you have?

____

____

7. Look in the telephone book under your county's name. What are three county departments?

a. ______________________________

b. ______________________________

c. ______________________________

Mayor-Council Plans of Local Governments

The most widely used type of local government is the **mayor-council plan.** There are two types of mayor-council governments. They are the strong mayor-council and the weak mayor-council.

The Strong Mayor

Usually larger cities have the **strong mayor-council plan**. This plan gives the mayor power to make decisions for the community. The mayor is the executive of the city. He or she is charged with making sure laws are enforced. The mayor needs the cooperation of the **council** to be successful. Council members represent various parts of the city, or **municipality.** The council is the lawmaking body of the city. The mayor is not a part of the legislative body.

Areas of the city have different problems or interests. Some areas may be wealthy, while other areas may be poor. One part of the city can be industrial or have more businesses than another part. Other sections of the city may have poor housing, better schools, better roads, or more or less crime. All of these issues are important to the people who elect their council members. It is necessary for the council members to represent the people who elected them to office. An elected official also needs to serve the best interests of the city.

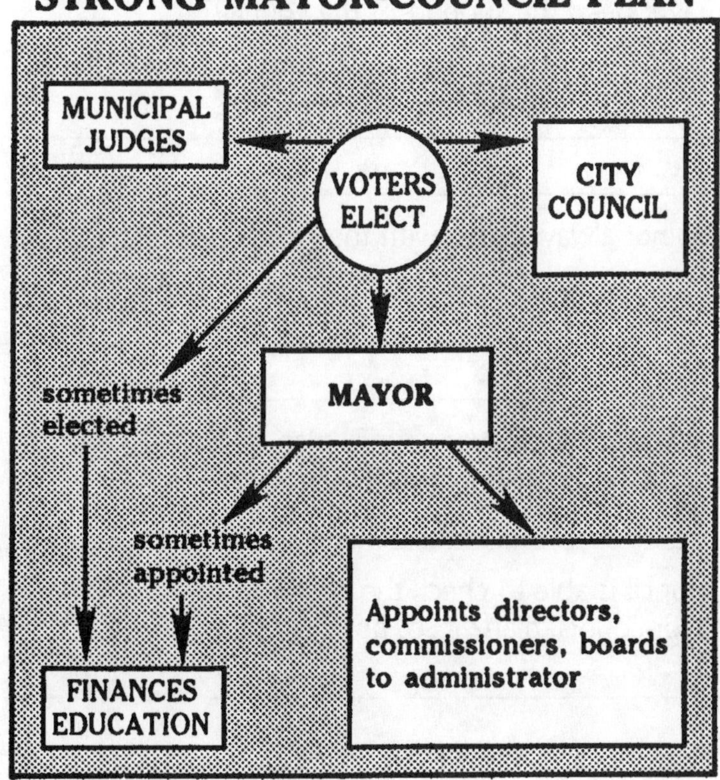

UNIT 8

The Weak Mayor

The **weak mayor-council plan** is a form of government in which power is shared between the mayor and the council. The city council is in charge of the government. The council appoints department heads to help in the day-to-day business of the city. The mayor has very little power and serves as the ceremonial (public relations) head of the government. The weak mayor plan is usually found in smaller cities.

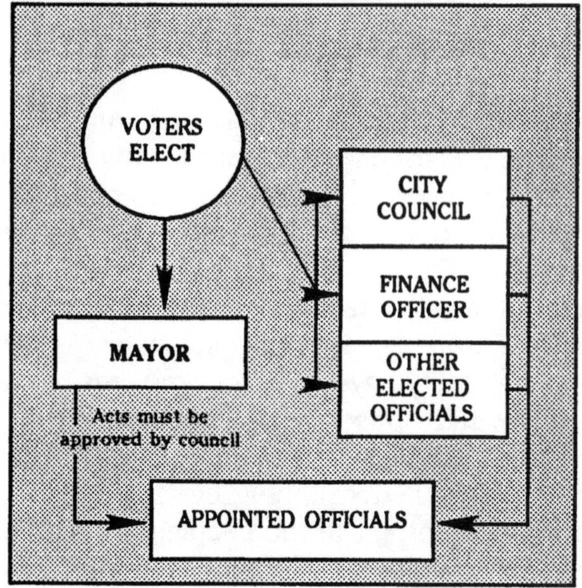

A **Special Thought Questions:** Write your answer to each question.

1. Why does the strong mayor need the support of the council?

____

____

____

2. City council members do not always agree with the ideas of the mayor. Explain.

____

____

3. Larger cities usually have the strong mayor-council plan. Smaller cities often have the weak mayor-council plan. Why?

____

4. Do you think the city council is able to check the power of the mayor in the strong mayor-council plan? If so, how? If not, why?

____

____

____

B Fill in each blank with the correct term. Choose the answer from the word box.

Word Box

cooperation	larger	ceremonial
weak mayor-council	two	strong mayor-council
weak	council	municipality
smaller	shared	

Mayor-Council Plans of Local Government

There are ________________ types of mayor-council local governments. They are the ________________ ________________ ________________ plan and the ________________ ________________ ________________ plan. The legislative (lawmaking) body is called the ________________. The mayor needs the ________________ of the council if he or she expects to be successful. The strong mayor-council plan is usually used in ________________ cities. Council members represent various parts of the ________________.

In the ________________ mayor-council plan, power is ________________ by the mayor and the council. Most of the power, however, is given to the city council. The mayor serves as the ________________ head of the government. The weak mayor plan is usually used in ________________ towns.

C Answer these questions.

1. Who is your mayor?

____

2. What kind of local government does your city or town have?

____

3. What type of services does your municipal government provide?

____

4. Do you think your municipal government should keep its form of government or change? Why?

____

____

The Council-Manager Government

The **council-manager system** is another type of local government. The council is elected by the people. It is the legislative branch of a city or town. Council members are in charge of making **policy**, or plans of action, and laws. The council hires a professional manager. The manager is a person with experience and training in government operations. The manager's job is to put the policies, established by the council, into effect.

The manager has some power over the budget. He or she can make recommendations to the council. It is important to remember that the manager's job is to take care of the day-to-day business of the city or town. If the manager does not do well, the council can dismiss (fire) him or her. Many cities have this form of government. A city may also have a mayor even if it has a manager.

The Commission-Type Government

The city of Galveston, Texas, was greatly damaged by a hurricane in 1900. Galveston had the weak mayor-council plan. When the disaster happened, the government was unable to deal with the severe problems that the city faced. A board of five commissioners was chosen to get things done. This was the beginning of the **commission-type government.**

The number of commissioners can vary from three to seven. The board of commissioners is elected by the people. The board serves as both the executive and legislative branches of government. Each commissioner specializes in one or more departments of the government. The board often chooses one of the members to act as the chairperson. This person may be given the title of mayor. The chairperson has no real power other than his or her job as commissioner. It is a ceremonial position for special events. In some cases, a mayor is elected in addition to the commissioners. The mayor, in this case, has no power. The city needs such a person to serve as the official of the city.

Summary of Local Government

People decide which government is best for them. Baltimore, Maryland, has a strong mayor-council plan; Los Angeles, California, has a weak mayor-council plan; Dallas, Texas, has the council-manager plan; and Portland, Oregon, has the commission plan. All of these cities are important urban communities. There are advantages and disadvantages to each form of government. Good local government requires qualified officials, good leadership, and most of all, concerned and involved citizens. Sometimes voters ignore local elections and vote only in national elections. This is unfortunate because local government is our first level of government—the level of government closest to us. It is worth our time and attention to select good leaders. These leaders have great impact on our everyday lives. They make decisions about police and fire protection, they are responsible for repairing and maintaining local roads, they establish rules for the kinds of buildings that can be built, and much more. Without good elected officials, city services can suffer, and the needs of residents will not be met.

Review Unit 8

A Write a paragraph in which you use the following words. The words can be used in any order.

council
policy
legislative
elected
manager
dismiss
budget
cooperate

B Write your answers to the questions.

1. Should all urban communities, villages, towns, and cities have one type of local government? Why or why not?

2. Many cities and towns continue to increase in population. What problems do you see as a result of that increase in size?

3. Cities often need money. Where should the money come from?

4. Choose a form of local government. Write one advantage and one disadvantage for that form of government.

C Read each clue. Then write the word being defined where it belongs in the puzzle. Use the words in the list.

manager	parish	council
commissioner	policy	cooperation
county	village	rural
levy	urban	state
municipality	unitary	

Local Government

ACROSS

4. city lawmaking body
5. elected county official
9. working together
10. outside the city; country
11. level of government below state
13. to place a tax
14. person hired, not elected, to run a local government

DOWN

1. a plan of action
2. the government with which the federal government shares power
3. urban political unit; city
6. another word for county
7. the smallest kind of community
8. only a central government; no lower levels
12. in the city

Pressure Groups

Very often groups of people have special interests such as better wages, wildlife, business, women's rights, the elderly, civil rights, and education. These groups are sometimes called **pressure groups.**

Not all of the groups are large. Some groups may have only a few members. Other interest groups are very large, with thousands of members.

Special-interest groups cannot pass laws. They can, however, use the media (radio, television, newspapers, and magazines) to bring attention to the ideas of their groups. This is what is meant by the term, the **third house**. Special-interest groups hope to convince the lawmakers to do what they want.

Lobbyists

The largest pressure groups, and those that have enough money, hire people to work for them. These people are well trained and know a great deal about the group they represent. They are called **lobbyists.** A lobbyist uses his or her influence to help the special-interest group get what it wants. The lobbyist can pressure the lawmakers because he or she may represent many voters in the special-interest group. Voters' opinions are very important to a **politician** (elected official). There are many issues that people are concerned about. Each group works hard to get changes made.

Pressure Groups—Good or Bad?

The big question about pressure groups has always been the same. Are these groups good or bad? Some groups have a lot of money. They get their money from contributions from people who agree with their cause. Lobby groups can give money to a politician for his or her next election. In return, they hope the politician will support their opinions. Giving money to a political campaign is not a crime. However, many people see this as the bad side of pressure groups. They believe that an official who takes money from pressure groups will feel obligated to support the groups' views.

There is a good side to pressure groups and lobbyists. Groups work hard to gather important information about their special interest. Public officials can talk to lobbyists and leaders of the pressure groups to hear what they have to say. By discussing the issues, a politician gets a chance to understand the facts. Government officials have many things to do. They may not be able to gather all the information they need to make informed decisions. Therefore, pressure groups or special-interest groups can be helpful in providing information. However, this information usually supports only one side of an issue.

Some attempts have been made to **regulate** (control) lobbying. Changes have been made in the laws. More changes may take place in the future.

UNIT 9

A Make a list of at least three special-interest groups that you know about. Why do you think each one is important?

1. ______________________________
2. ______________________________
3. ______________________________

B Decide whether each statement is *True* or *False.* Write your answer on the line.

______ 1. Congress is the lawmaking body of our federal government.

______ 2. *Third house* refers to pressure groups and lobbying.

______ 3. Some special-interest groups have thousands of members.

______ 4. A lobbyist is hired to represent all the people.

______ 5. In our system of government, people have the right to join special-interest groups.

______ 6. Politicians care little about voters' opinions.

______ 7. People give money to special-interest groups.

______ 8. Special-interest groups cannot contribute money to political campaigns.

______ 9. According to the law, special-interest groups must be represented by a lobbyist.

______ 10. A lobbyist tries to influence lawmakers' decisions.

C Complete the following sentences.

1. Lobbying is good because ______________________________

____

2. Lobbying is bad because ______________________________

____

D **Special Thought Questions:** Write your answers on your own paper.

1. Good government must have honest lawmakers. Lobbying makes it possible for some lawmakers to get into trouble. What do you think should be done about lobbying?
2. The problem with pressure groups is that they care only about their own special interest. What is best for them may not be best for all people. What do you think?

Public Opinion

The first ten amendments to the Constitution are called the **Bill of Rights.** The early leaders of the nation wanted to be sure that the rights of the people would be protected. Included in the first of these amendments is freedom of speech. Freedom of speech allows people to talk about the things that are important to them. What people say about issues and policies is called **public opinion.** It has been said that the federal government is shaped by public opinion. Different people, not necessarily groups of people, have opinions about how and what the government should do. Older people might want more health care, younger people might want more jobs, and a young family might want day care for young children. Elected public officials pay close attention to the opinions of the public.

How Public Opinion Is Shaped

There are several ways that public opinion is formed. Mass media play a major role in shaping opinions. Newspapers, magazines, radio, and television report the news to the American public. In addition, the media provide editorials, or opinions and comments, on news events and issues. How much influence the media has on public opinion is hard to say.

Many polls are taken to measure public opinion. Polling is a big business. A variety of polls ask people questions about a certain issue. The answers to those questions are used to measure public opinion. How accurate (correct) are the polls? The answer is debatable.

During election years, polls are taken often by the candidates and by news organizations. Such polls give the candidates and the public a general idea of which candidate is ahead and which issues are important. Sometimes polls are correct in their findings; other times they are not.

Influences Affecting Public Opinion

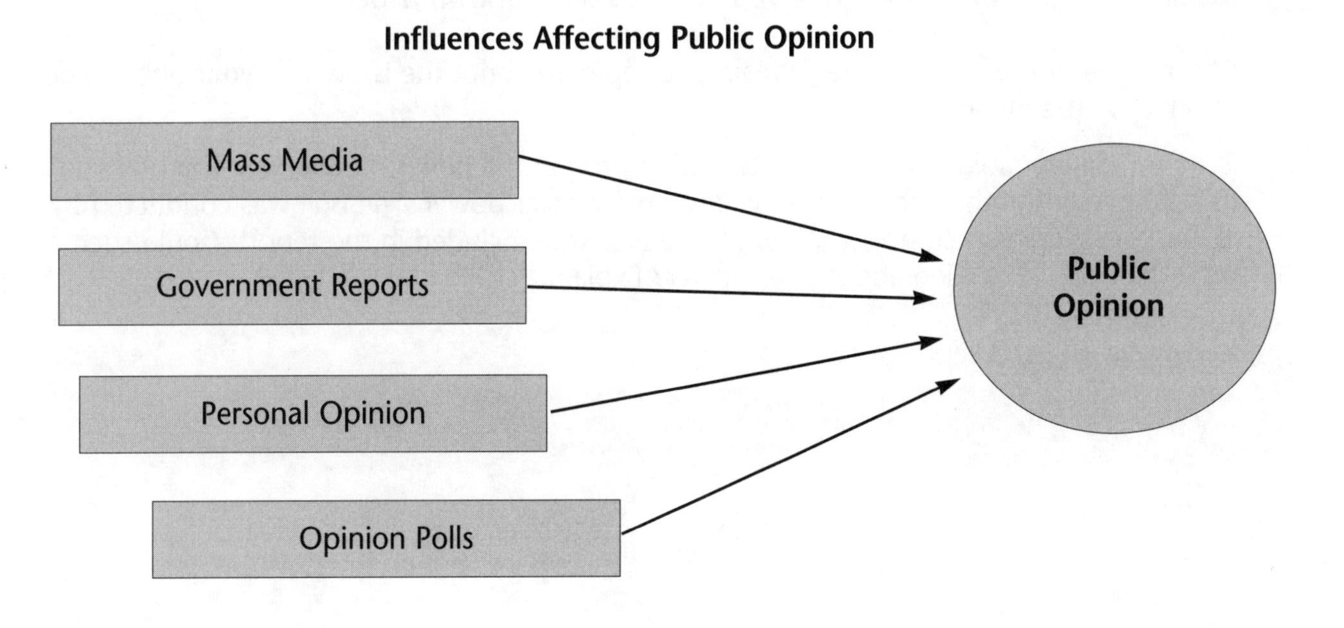

UNIT 9

A Listed below are some important issues that face our country today. What is your opinion about each one? Use A (Agree), B (Disagree), or C (No Opinion). Write your answer on the line in front of each statement.

_____ 1. The government wastes too much money.

_____ 2. English should be made the official language of the United States.

_____ 3. More work opportunities are needed for women and minority groups.

_____ 4. Drug dealers should go to jail for no less than twenty-five years.

_____ 5. The school year should be increased to eleven months of the year.

_____ 6. The minimum wage should be raised even higher.

_____ 7. Illegal immigration should be stopped.

_____ 8. Health care needs to be provided for everyone.

_____ 9. Automobiles are safe to drive.

_____ 10. A strong defense, although expensive, is good for the people of our country.

_____ 11. Immigrants take jobs from American citizens.

_____ 12. People on welfare who can work should work.

_____ 13. American troops should not be sent on peace-keeping missions in other countries.

_____ 14. All people have the right to a good education.

_____ 15. Less money should be spent on the space program.

B **Special Thought Questions:** Write your answers on your own paper.

1. Choose one of the issues above. Explain your opinion about the issue. Has your opinion been affected by the media?
2. In a newspaper, radio, magazine, or television program, a poll is mentioned. The poll said that 60 percent of the people asked wanted more solar power. The poll was conducted by a major public opinion company. All of the details were included in the report. Could such a poll affect public opinion about solar power? Explain.

Propaganda

Propaganda, by definition, is the effort to spread a belief or an opinion about a certain issue. Commercial advertisers, the media, governments, pressure groups, and public officials all use propaganda. Propaganda, in itself, is not necessarily bad. It is simply an attempt to get people to think a certain way about something.

Propaganda is most effective when people are not well informed. People lead busy lives. Work, children, school, recreation, and home responsibilities take up a lot of time. It is not easy to study all of the facts about every issue. It is easier for a busy individual to listen to one person than to hear many ideas and then form his or her own opinion. Listening to a brief news broadcast, quickly glancing through the newspaper, watching a few TV shows, and reading popular magazines are not enough to be well informed.

Types of Propaganda

There are many propaganda techniques. The following list gives some examples:

A. *Name Calling:* Names such as *left-wing, communists, conservatives, liberals, racist, greedy,* and so forth are used to describe something or someone. These names suggest that something is bad about a person or an issue.

B. *Card Stacking:* All facts presented about an issue or a person are either good or bad. Both sides of the story are not given.

C. *Glittering Generalities:* Words are used that mean little but sound good. "He is a good American" and "We only want what's best for our country" are two examples.

D. *Transfer:* Important symbols like the American flag or Uncle Sam are used on printed materials. These symbols mean a great deal to most Americans. When people see a symbol that is important to them, they may pay more attention to what a group or person is saying.

E. *Testimonials: A* well-known person such as a basketball player, tennis player, movie star, or singer is shown supporting a person or an issue. If the well-known person is liked by the people, they may support the issue the celebrity represents.

F. *The Bandwagon:* This technique tries to convince the public that everyone else is for a certain issue and they should be for it, too. People do not like to feel like they are being left out.

G. *Plain Folks:* This technique is used when a very successful person wants your vote or support on an issue. He or she says "I am just like you are ... just an ordinary person trying to make a living." This person hopes to gain people's trust by giving the impression that he or she is just like them.

UNIT 9

Review Unit 9

A Complete the following exercise.

List seven propaganda techniques (methods).

1. ______________________________
2. ______________________________
3. ______________________________
4. ______________________________
5. ______________________________
6. ______________________________
7. ______________________________

B Read each of the following messages. Identify the propaganda technique used in each. Write your answer on the line.

1. Polls indicate that 85 percent of the voters support our candidate. The newspapers say he is the best person for the job. Join your friends and neighbors and vote for the candidate that everyone agrees can do the job.

   ____

2. Our candidate is a devoted mother. She values her family and her country. She thinks of her country as part of her family. She will work to make her country strong.

   ____

3. As a child, I had a newspaper route. The money I earned helped feed my family. Like your family, my family struggled to make ends meet. Because I have had the same experiences as you, I can represent your interests in Congress.

   ____

4. I hold the Constitution in front of you. This is what our country is about. I support the Constitution and what it symbolizes for all Americans.

   ____

C Look at the list of propaganda techniques. Choose three of them and write an example of a commercial, slogan, or phrase using that technique.

1. ______________________________

____

2. ______________________________

____

3. ______________________________

____

D Write your answers to these questions.

1. Pressure groups make it harder for lawmakers to do their jobs. What do you think?

____

____

2. Some pressure groups have millions of dollars to spend. Lobbyists are paid very high salaries. Is that how our democratic system should work? What do you think?

____

____

3. Public opinion, right or wrong, shapes public policy. Should we leave it up to the elected officials to do what they think is best?

____

____

4. There are polls for just about everything. Is it possible for polls to be the real measure of public opinion? What do you think?

____

____

5. The mass media gives us the news as they see it. Do you see any problems with that kind of reporting? Explain.

____

____

REVIEW

Review Units 7–9

Write the word or phrase from the box that completes each sentence.

Word Box

politician	taxes	opinions
propaganda	lobbyist	mass media
governor	council	bicameral
county	unitary	urban area

1. A ______________________ hopes to influence lawmakers to vote for the interests of his or her group.

2. Voters' ______________________ are important to elected officials.

3. A person who serves the community as an elected official is called a ______________________.

4. Newspapers, radio, and television are examples of ______________________ ______________________.

5. One way of presenting information about issues is through advertising techniques called ______________________.

6. States have the right to levy ______________________.

7. All states except Nebraska have a ______________________ legislature.

8. State government is a ______________________ system of government.

9. The level of government below state government is ______________________ government.

10. A legislative body of a city is often called a ______________________.

11. A city is known as an ______________________ ______________________.

12. A ______________________ is the head of the executive branch of a state's government.

End-of-Book Test

T E S T

A Write *True* or *False* on the line before each statement.

_______________ **1.** Commercial advertisers, the media, government, and public officials all use propaganda.

_______________ **2.** In a state, the county government is the next unit of government below state government.

_______________ **3.** The first elected legislature was the Virginia House of Burgesses.

_______________ **4.** The Articles of Confederation provided an effective form of government for many years.

_______________ **5.** Great Britain has a unitary form of government.

_______________ **6.** When the Constitution was written, no compromises were made.

_______________ **7.** There are two branches in the federal government of the United States.

_______________ **8.** The courts can override a presidential veto.

_______________ **9.** There are over fifty amendments to the Constitution.

_______________ **10.** George Washington was unanimously elected President.

_______________ **11.** The two-party system developed early in the history of our federal government.

_______________ **12.** Minor political parties frequently win elections.

_______________ **13.** Congress is an example of a unicameral legislature.

_______________ **14.** A senator has a longer term of office than a member of the House of Representatives.

_______________ **15.** States are divided into congressional districts.

_______________ **16.** The Speaker of the House is a member of the minority party.

_______________ **17.** In the House, there are two representatives from each state.

_______________ **18.** Committees do most of the actual work in Congress.

_______________ **19.** Presidents may serve any number of terms.

_______________ **20.** The President is a leader in foreign policy.

_______________ **21.** The Supreme Court tries appeals cases.

_______________ **22.** Less serious crimes are called misdemeanors.

_______________ **23.** The governor is the chief executive of a state.

_______________ **24.** All but one state legislature are bicameral.

_______________ **25.** Propaganda is most effective when people are not well informed.

TEST

B Read each clue. Write the name of the person being described. Choose from the names in the box.

Aaron Burr	Bill Clinton
James Madison	Thomas Jefferson
Alexander Hamilton	Franklin D. Roosevelt
Benjamin Franklin	John Locke
George Washington	John Adams

1. I suggested the Albany Plan in New York in 1754.

____

2. The Declaration of Independence was written by me.

____

3. My philosophy influenced the writings of Thomas Jefferson.

____

4. I had the same number of electoral votes as Thomas Jefferson in the election of 1800.

____

5. The Bill of Rights was something I helped write.

____

6. I was chosen to be the first President of the United States.

____

7. I was selected to be the first Vice President.

____

8. My presidency lasted for fourteen years.

____

9. In Washington's cabinet, I was the first Secretary of the Treasury.

____

10. I was governor of Arkansas before I became President.

____

C Number the following items 1, 2, 3, 4, 5, or 6 to show the order in which things happened.

_____ Declaration of Independence

_____ State constitutions

_____ John Locke's philosophy

_____ Benjamin Franklin's Albany Plan

_____ Constitution of the United States

_____ Articles of Confederation

D Write *E* for executive branch, *L* for legislative branch, and *J* for judicial branch to show which branch of government is being described.

_____ **1.** This body can levy taxes on imported goods.

_____ **2.** Rulings are in the form of opinions in the Supreme Court.

_____ **3.** Bills can be vetoed here.

_____ **4.** Secretaries offer advice and run departments in this branch.

_____ **5.** Only this group can declare war.

_____ **6.** This branch develops and carries out foreign policy.

_____ **7.** Treaties with other countries are approved in this branch.

_____ **8.** The members in this branch hold their position for life.

_____ **9.** If money is needed, this branch can borrow it.

_____ **10.** This group might uphold a lower court's decision.

_____ **11.** The commander in chief is in this branch.

_____ **12.** Appointments are approved in this body.

TEST

E Write the letter of the best answer to each question on the line.

_____ **1.** With what other governments does the federal government share power?
- **a.** no other governments
- **b.** state governments
- **c.** foreign governments
- **d.** municipalities

_____ **2.** What did each state have to have before it could become a state?
- **a.** a governor
- **b.** local governments
- **c.** a constitution
- **d.** free trade

_____ **3.** What state is the only one to have a unicameral legislature?
- **a.** California
- **b.** Indiana
- **c.** Kansas
- **d.** Nebraska

_____ **4.** Why is the job of governor sometimes called a stepping stone?
- **a.** A governor must step up to the needs of the people.
- **b.** A governor can step over the state legislature.
- **c.** A governor often moves on to a higher office.
- **d.** A governor may conduct ceremonies on the steps of the state house.

_____ **5.** What are most state legislative bodies called?
- **a.** the legislature
- **b.** the state assembly
- **c.** the senate
- **d.** the chambers

_____ **6.** What is money given to states by the federal government called?
- **a.** taxes
- **b.** grants in aid
- **c.** states' rights
- **d.** levies

_____ **7.** A lieutenant governor is similar to what other elected office?
- **a.** senator
- **b.** vice president
- **c.** governor
- **d.** mayor

_____ **8.** What are two other names for *county?*
- **a.** legislature, courts
- **b.** borough, parish
- **c.** urban, rural
- **d.** state, local

_____ **9.** What name is often given an elected county official?
- **a.** mayor
- **b.** clerk
- **c.** commissioner
- **d.** executive

_____ **10.** How are most cities and towns governed?
- **a.** by a president and senate
- **b.** by a governor and assembly
- **c.** by a mayor and council
- **d.** by a mayor and treasurer

F Decide what kind of propaganda is being used in each example. Write the letter of its name on the line.

a. Name Calling
b. Card Stacking
c. Glittering Generalities
d. Transfer
e. Testimonials
f. The Bandwagon
g. Plain Folks

_____ 1. I'm just like one of you. I work hard for a living. I know how difficult it is to raise a family these days.

_____ 2. Mr. Jones has an eagle and a flag on the posters he is putting up announcing his candidacy.

_____ 3. I want to introduce to you a great American. A person who loves this country with all her heart. She is someone who is honest and hard-working.

_____ 4. My political opponent is soft on crime. He wants your money because he is a "tax and spender." We don't want this kind of person in our government.

_____ 5. Polls show that our candidate is leading by a wide margin in recent opinion polls. Her popularity is growing daily. Won't you join the rest of us and give her your support?

G Write your answer to each question.

1. What are two examples of mass media?

____

____

2. What is one special interest a lobbyist might pressure Congress about?

____

____

3. What might a researcher use as the subject of a poll?

____

____

4. What kind of propaganda was used in a television commercial you have seen recently? What was the commercial for?

____

____

T E S T

H Write the word from the box that correctly completes each sentence.

Word Box

Congress	appeal	Bill
judicial	Federalists	urban
amendments	census	candidates
poll	bicameral	governor
veto	ruling	Senate

1. The upper house of Congress is called the ______________________.
2. The counting of the population every ten years is known as the ______________________.
3. Those in John Adams's time who favored a strong central government were called ______________________.
4. The Supreme Court's power to declare a law unconstitutional is known as ______________________ review.
5. Those running for elective office are called ______________________.
6. Additions to the Constitution are called ______________________.
7. A two-house legislature is said to be ______________________.
8. The chief executive of a state is known as the ______________________.
9. A sampling of public opinion is called a ______________________.
10. An opinion issued by the Supreme Court is also known as a ______________________.
11. A city is known as an ______________________ area.
12. The President's decision to turn down a bill is called a ______________________.
13. The legislative branch of the federal government is known as ______________________.
14. The first ten amendments to the Constitution are called the ______________________ of Rights.
15. To ask for a review by a higher court is known as an ______________________.

Glossary

GLOSSARY

A

amendments: additions to the Constitution

Anti-Federalists: political party that favored strong state government

appeal: to ask for a review by the higher courts

Articles of Confederation: government prior to ratification of the Constitution

assassination: when an important person or public official is killed

associate justices: eight justices who also serve on the Supreme Court

B

bicameral: two houses (legislative)

bill: legislation that can become a law

C

cabinet: advisers to the president

candidate: one who seeks a public office

case: a civil or criminal matter that must be decided in the courts

census: taken once every ten years to count the people in the United States

central government: another name for the federal government

ceremonial: special events; represents our country

checks and balances: when each branch of government, the executive, judicial, and legislative, has power to stop a branch from getting too much power

chief justice: the leader of the Supreme Court

circuit: state courts organized in a geographical region to deal with major criminal cases

citizen: a person born in a country, or becomes a citizen through proper channels (naturalization) who has rights

civil: cases that deal with problems between people

commander in chief: President; civilian; in charge of the armed forces

compromise: an agreement between two sides with different ideas

confederate: gives more power to the states and less to the central government

Congress: legislative branch of the United States; two houses; bicameral

congressmen/congresswomen: members of the House of Representatives

conservative: make changes more slowly; less government

Constitution: the supreme law of the United States

constitutional rights: rights of individuals spelled out in the Bill of Rights and other sections of the Constitution

council: legislative—local government

D

delegates: representatives for an area of people

Democratics: political party; identified as more liberal

departments: divisions in the executive branch that do the work to run the country

districts: geographic divisions of a state that contain (as nearly as possible) equal population to elect members of the House of Representatives

E

electors: those who were chosen to be the official voters in a presidential election

enforce: to be sure that the laws are obeyed

executive: law-enforcing branch of government

F

federal: central government

Federalists: political party that favored strong central government

filibuster: to talk a bill to death (only in the Senate)

foreign policy: a plan that enables our country to promote our interests and better understand the interests of other countries

G

governor: chief executive of a state

H

House of Representatives: lower house based on population; 435 members, one from each district; two-year term

I

interpret: explain

J

judicial: court system; interprets and administers the law

judicial review: power to declare a law unconstitutional

L

legislative: lawmaking branch of government

GLOSSARY

legislative districts: divisions within a state to elect state officials

levy: to place a tax

liberal: want changes more quickly; more government

lieutenant governor: leader of the state senate in some states that have a lieutenant governor

limited government: shared power between federal and state governments

lobbyists: those who represent interest groups

local government: government at the lowest level; towns and cities; fast action; serves needs of people

lower house: House of Representatives

M

magistrate: a judge who tries minor cases

majority party: over 50% (number of members)

mass media: the various forms of presenting information; radio, television, etc.

minority party: less than 50% of members

misdemeanors: minor crimes; penalty is less serious

municipality: urban political unit

O

opinion: ruling; decision given by the Supreme Court; not a verdict

P

Parliament: British lawmaking branch; combines executive and legislative branches

political parties: organizations that have certain political ideas

politician: person interested in serving the community in an elected capacity

polls: sampling the public to see what people think about certain issues

president pro tempore: takes the place of the Vice-President during his or her absence from the Senate

public office: a service to people

public opinion: how people feel about certain issues

R

reapportionment: process done after census every ten years; to be sure the districts are equal in population

representation: electing an official to speak for the people and to be equally represented

Republicans: political party; identified as more conservative

revenue sharing: money that comes back to states from the federal government

ruling: decision

rural: countryside (away from the city)

S

secretary: in charge of an executive department

Senate: 100 members (two senators from each state; six-year term; upper house)

separation of powers: when each of the three branches of government has certain responsibilities and cannot interfere with the other two

speaker: leader of the House of Representatives; chosen by the majority party

state government: government that runs state affairs

Supreme Court: highest court of appeal

T

term: time period a person is elected to an office

third house: lobbying; pressure groups

treaties: agreements with other countries

two-party system: those parties narrow in scope; issue-oriented; two major political parties in the country

U

unanimous: 100% agreement

unconstitutional: against the Constitution

unicameral: one house (legislature)

unitary: only a central government; no lower levels of government required

uphold: remain the same; no change

upper house: the Senate

urban: city

V

verdict: a decision of guilty or innocent of a crime or misdemeanor

veto: the President's power to turn down a bill

vulnerable: open for attack